CHRISTIAN BELIEF AND SCIENCE

A Reconciliation and a Partnership

CHRISTIAN BELIEF
AND
SCIENCE

A Reconciliation and a Partnership

BY

ROBERT E. D. CLARK

MUHLENBERG PRESS – PHILADELPHIA

CONTENTS

ACKNOWLEDGEMENTS

GRATEFUL acknowledgements are due to the following for permission to quote. To Messrs George Allen and Unwin, Ltd, for the quotations from Bertrand Russell's *Why I am not a Christian* on p. 8 and from Dr Waismann's chapter in *Contemporary British Philosophy* on p. 12; to Messrs G. Bell and Sons, Ltd, for the quotation from Professor Butterfield's *Christianity and History* on p. 55; to the Cambridge University Press for the quotation from Professor Whitehead's *Science and the Modern World* on p. 94; to Messrs W. Heffer and Sons Ltd (Cambridge) for the quotation from Job of Edessa's *Encyclopedia of Philosophical and Natural Sciences . . . or Book of Treasures* on p. 36; to the Sheldon Press for the quotation from R. H. Murray's *Science and Scientists in the Nineteenth Century* on p. 93; to the Society of Chemical Industry for the quotation from an article from Professor J. Kendall on p. 101 and to Messrs Watts and Co. Ltd for the quotations from Professor Darlington's *Conflict of Science and Society* (Conway Memorial Lecture, 1948) on pp. 88 and 133.

I

BELIEF
In a Scientific Age

Many of us were brought up as Christians. But the world in which we live has filled our minds with doubts and forebodings.

Nostalgically we think of old-fashioned evangelists urging people to "believe and be saved". Has such preaching any relevance in an age of science? Can a man accept Christianity, unquestioningly, in obedience to a command? Can he *make* himself believe when his mind is filled with doubts?

Belief—Two Kinds

As a start let us consider the two words with which religion is so much concerned—"belief" and "faith". What do they mean?

They have reference, firstly, to statements of fact— of the kind that lies beyond the evidence. We speak of believing that the earth has a core of molten iron because no one has dug down to see, but not of believing that $2+2=4$, for this is demonstrable. "Faith is the [inward] assurance of things hoped for, the conviction

B   I

[of the truth] of things not seen" (Heb. 11.1).[1]
Secondly, we speak of "belief" and "faith" in connection
with perseverence and devotion to a cause or to a
person in whom men trust. Here the intellectual proposition ("The cause is worth while", "The leader of
my nation is trustworthy", "The Party is never wrong")
is almost forgotten and what is, from one point of view,
intellectual faith becomes identified with its power to
inspire. In this sense Christians speak both of "belief"
and of "faith" in Christ and, using the word in the
same sense, Old Testament heroes are said to have
done great deeds "by faith" (Heb. 11).

Faith then has two connotations. Bearing this in
mind, we may ask, firstly, whether it is now harder
for people to accept beliefs than it was in former ages
and, secondly, whether they find it harder to become
devoted to causes.

Belief not Outmoded

To start with the first point: it is commonly supposed
that men, today, are more critical than formerly, and
that, in consequence, they find belief more difficult.

This notion is certainly open to doubt. In the course
of elementary chemistry lectures some years back, the
writer mentioned, quite speculatively, a theory advanced

[1] It is sometimes said that "belief" (Gk. *pistis*, verb, *pisteuo*) and
"faith" (Gk. *pistis*) are used only in a special theological sense in the
New Testament, so that it is inappropriate to look for non-theological
parallels. This, however, is a mistake—"one *believeth* that he may eat
all things" (Rom. 14.2); the devils also *believe*, and tremble" (Jas.
2.9), etc.

2

by Callendar[1] to the effect that the increase in the temperature of the world in recent decades is due to the increase in the carbon dioxide content of the air as a result of the burning of fossil fuels by man on an ever-increasing scale. He mentioned it in the spirit of "just possible—not proved—the rise in temperature is not known to apply all over the earth anyway". At the end of the session the students had a chance to mention this theory, if they remembered it, in an answer to an examination question. Nearly all remembered it, and those who did, without exception, asserted that the hypothesis was true, just as if there had been no shadow of doubt whatever! In view of such experiences, which every teacher could parallel, it is hard to think that the teaching of science makes young people unduly critical of the beliefs they accept. Indeed, so long as the ideas presented to them hold together they seem only too ready to believe. Witness the widely held conviction, often held with fervour, that man will conquer space in the comparatively near future—an idea that would have seemed stark madness prior to World War II.

Or, take the innumerable errors which are copied from one scientific text-book into another—some of them hoary with age.[2] They are accepted by generation

[1] G. S. Callendar, *Quart. Jour. Roy. Meteor Soc.*, 1938, **64**, 223.
[2] F. A. Paneth (*Nature*, 1937, **139**, 222) quotes G. Ch. Lichtenstein, one-time Professor of physics at Göttingen, as saying: "Perhaps Hamlet is right that there are more things in heaven and earth than are dreamed of in our philosophy; but on the other hand it may be said that there are a good many things in our natural philosophy books of which neither in heaven nor on earth any trace can be found". Many text-book "facts" are seen through the rosy hues of one theory or another—e.g. the older but wrong view of the functioning of the

after generation of students and duly reproduced in examinations. Only on the rarest occasions do people find them difficult to swallow or bother to check their truth in the laboratory.

Yet again, take some of the strange results of modern physics—queerer by far and quite as hard to understand as anything the Church has taught—the notion that there is a maximum velocity faster than which it is impossible for anything to travel, the idea of finite but unbounded space, or the theory that there are positive charges at the centres of atoms, extremely close together, yet for some reason not flying apart. It is not often that we hear these beliefs questioned, though they are hard to believe and seem to conflict with common sense. How many boys and girls in our schools ever think to question modern views on the structure of the atom, for instance, even though they have known for years that positive charges repel one another?

It may be replied, of course, that the beliefs of which we have spoken are not to be compared with religious faith. People are prepared to accept what scientists tell them about this or that, but they would be equally ready to drop these theories if scientists were to change

---

frog's heart (G. E. H. Foxton, *New Biology*, **12**, 113). Sometimes mistakes are simply copied—the figure for the heat conductivity of plaster of Paris was determined in 1896 and the value given in standard books, with the decimal in the wrong place, till 1950 (*Nature*, 1957, **179**, 1187). Sometimes a general law leads one to expect a certain result which happens to be false in the simplest cases (e.g. the action of nitrous acid on methylamine—see *Nature*, 1947, **160**, 406). For many further examples taken from chemistry books see the series of articles on Text-book Errors in the *Journal of Chemical Education* for recent years.

their minds. No one would give his life for the opinion that the temperature of the earth is rising because of the fuel we burn, or for the belief that objects cannot travel faster than light. Is it fair to compare scientific theory with religious faith?

Perhaps not. Yet the comparison is sometimes freely drawn by scientists themselves. A well-known text-book puts it bluntly: "Relativity is now accepted as a faith. It is inadvisable to devote attention to its paradoxical aspects".[1] Many scientists deplore such statements, but it is clear that many do not.

Faith in a Cause

But let us turn to more deeply rooted beliefs—beliefs that involve the perseverance and devotion of which we have spoken. Does the civilization in which we live make it harder or easier to accept them? Certainly not harder. Passionate beliefs in fascism and in communism have spread like wildfire in our century, to say nothing of a thousand lesser known faiths. Fascism arose in one of the most highly industrialized and educationally advanced countries in the world. In view of this fact, can we say that the coming of a scientific age makes faith of this kind harder to acquire?

Or again, it is hardly possible to take an interest in science at all without gaining the impression that positive faith among scientists is amazingly prevalent. The faith that has led to the determination of the

[1] R. A. Houstoun, *A Treatise on Light* (Longmans), 1938, p. 502.

structures of vitamin B12 and insulin, to radar,[1] to the separation of isotopes on an industrial scale, to the unleashing of atomic energy[2] or to the launching of huge rockets[3] and, ultimately, earth satellites and moon rockets, surely compares favourably with anything to be found in past history. Only a living faith can turn the almost unbelievable proposition "This is possible" into an actuality—especially when the innovator knows that very few people take him seriously.

In these and many other instances we see evidence of almost unimaginable perseverance in the face of the greatest and most disheartening odds. We have but to read, say, the eleventh chapter of the Epistle to the Hebrews, to learn that this is also the stuff out of which religious faith is made.

Language and Belief

Belief, then, is not harder to acquire than formerly—perhaps it is even easier. Of course, the modern man likes to see ideas dressed up in a language with which he is familiar. But was not the same true in past ages also?

In some of the creeds and ancient formularies of the Church we see relics of how Christians met the thought-forms of a previous age—of how, for example,

[1] R. Watson-Watt [Sir], *Three Steps to Victory*, 1957.
[2] A. H. Compton, in his fascinating book *Atomic Quest*, 1956. repeatedly speaks of the faith and vision that was involved. "Time and time again", he says, ". . . we found that seemingly by chance we had made the right choices, avoiding difficulties that no one had foreseen" (p. 170).
[3] W. Dornberger, *V2*, Eng. Trans. 1954; W. von Braun, "Reminiscences of German Rocketry", in *Jour. Brit. Interplanetary Soc.*, 1956, **15**, 125.

when the doctrine of procession in the psychology of Aristotle was in the ascendant, Christians used the words, "proceeding from the Father and the Son" in order to explain, as best they could, a truth of their religion.[1]

In the same way, in the late Middle Ages, Aquinas sought to bring Christianity to terms with the newly discovered classical knowledge which had taken the world by storm. Christians hold that it is part of the Church's job in every age to try to make the message of Christianity intelligible.

But can this be done today? Whatever the answer to this question, we may certainly conclude that if religious ideas could be presented in an intelligible form to our generation, men would not find it any harder to gain a positive religious faith than in former ages. For the evidence shows that nothing has happened to man's mental endowment to make faith a thing of the past.

Of course, difficulties fairly bristle ahead. Can Christians even hope to put the Christian gospel into scientific terms—or terms intelligible to a technological generation—without making it look ridiculous? Science and theology have long seen the parting of their ways. Their modes of thought are different. Their language is different. Is reconciliation possible?

[1] De L. E. O'Leary, *Arabic Thought and its Place in History*, 1939.

II

SOURCES OF KNOWLEDGE

On Rationalists and Reason

SOME people call themselves Rationalists. It is explained
that this word is intended to convey a belief that reason
—but especially reason of the kind that is used in
science—is man's only reliable guide.[1] Rationalists hold
that the human mind can possess no certain knowledge
save that which comes through reason and the senses.
They hold, therefore, that we should not accept any
opinion that is unreasonable, irrational or unscientific.
And it is here, they think, that religion fails. Religion
pretends to offer a certainty that is not squarely based
on reason.

All this sounds plausible enough. But, lest it should
be thought that religion is anti-rational, it ought in
fairness to be said that in all ages Christians, in particular, have thought highly of reason. Much of the Bible
is written in the style of "Come now and let us reason
together". Jesus taught men to worship the Lord with

[1] "A habit of basing convictions upon evidence, and of giving to
them only that degree of certainty which the evidence warrants
would, if it became general, cure most of the ills from which the world
is suffering"—Bertrand Russell in the Preface to *Why I am not a
Christian*, (Allen & Unwin) 1958. Other prominent Rationalists have
made similar statements.

their minds as well as with their other faculties, and St Peter urges men to stir up their minds. Unreasoning men could not obey such precepts.

Reason is undoubtedly important—everyone is in agreement here. Yet it is surprisingly difficult to be definite and clear as to what we mean by reason. The definitions in dictionaries are often tautologous. "To reason" is "to use the faculty of reason, to come to a conclusion as the result of reasoning, etc." Hardly enlightening! "To think consecutively, coherently or logically" is about as near as we shall get to a definition —inadequate though it be.

So by reasoning we mean at least this, that we arrange our thoughts, not at random, but in order; if possible with due regard to the rules of logic, each thought suggesting the one that follows. And some might add that "objective fact" should usually be the basis of our train of reasoning and that the last thought in the train should be by way of a "conclusion".

Reason's Limitations

Self-discipline of this kind is an excellent habit. But is it necessary to suppose that the ability to arrange thoughts is more important than other faculties? Reason is certainly not an infallible guide to knowledge. The story of science is one long story of how, again and again, reason led to wrong conclusions—such conclusions far outnumbering correct ones.

Again, how far is reason a serious factor in the lives of most of us—even of Rationalists? When we go shopping we rarely reason with ourselves consciously. We do not say: "I will purchase this *because* I saw an advertisement for it". We take good care not to get run over in traffic, but we do not consciously reason about the ways and means of crossing roads with the least possible danger to ourselves and others.

The same applies to most human relationships. "Our likings for other people . . . are never sufficiently founded upon reason," writes Fales. "When we meet someone, something snaps and a specific relation is established."[1] Likewise, as Helmholtz pointed out, when we recognise a friend we do not reason about our recognition of him. How hard it would be to prove by reason alone that a person is Mr. So-and-so and not a neighbour who is like him!

Again, reason is rarely of help to lovers who wish to know whether they are really in love. It does not enable us to enjoy good music or art or scenery. For the most part our emotions work quite well without it—there are times, in fact, when reasoning can destroy a beautiful experience.

Or take memory of time sequence. We may feel sure that we entered one building *before* and not *after* another. But why are we sure? Why is it that in our memories we place events in an ordered sequence? Suppose we are contradicted—what possible reasons can we give for the correctness of the order of events about which we are so certain? None, surely, that would convince someone who did not wish to be convinced.

[1] Walter Fales, *Wisdom and Responsibility*, 1946, p. 17.

Consider, in fact, any memory. How can we prove by reason only that it is not the memory of a dream? And even if it is—how can reason assure us that our memory of a dream that we really *did* dream is correct?

In these and many other instances we only use reason when we are perplexed by doubt. And the result, when reason has to be called in, is often less certain and less satisfying than when reason is not invoked.

But only occasionally do we find anything to reason about with profit. We reason about politics, seeking to figure out how the community will benefit if a certain policy is acted upon. We are offered employment and we try to discover by reason—by putting together the facts about the prospects, the satisfaction it will give us, the salary and so on—whether we should accept it. Reason is particularly valuable if we have to make difficult decisions. That is why we regard it as one of the guiding principles of life. Yet on the whole we do not use it overmuch.

Reason in Science

Even in science, reason has a much less important part to play than is often supposed. Science was unable to develop at all until the too high regard in which reason was held in the Middle Ages had been overthrown. It is to logicians and philosophers that we must look for the vigorous defence of reason rather than to scientists—many of whom have attacked its pretences with the utmost vigour. Schiller, for example, urges strongly that logic is of little use in productive scientific thinking.[1] Dr. F. Waismann, a mathematician, in attacking the vogue for clear thinking among contemporary philosophers, expresses himself equally vigorously: "There is nothing like clear thinking to protect one from making discoveries. It is all very well to talk of clarity, but when it becomes an obsession it is liable to nip the living thought in the bud. . . No great discoverer has acted in accordance with the motto, 'Everything that can be said can be said clearly.' And some of the greatest discoveries have emerged from a sort of primordial fog. (Something to be said for the fog. For my part, I've always suspected that clarity is the last refuge of those with nothing to say.)"[2]

Taken together, such facts must make what is called Rationalism seem a little odd. Why do men offer such deference to rationality? Not because they make great use of it. Why then? Because it is the highest faculty with which the human mind is endowed? But is it? Will reason support this claim?

We shall shortly see that it most certainly will not.

Reason By-passed

Reason is one avenue to knowledge. But it is an odd fact that even when knowledge comes to us through the senses, it often by-passes the reasoning mind altogether.

Imagine the following experiment. I take two one-

[1] F. S. C. Schiller, "Scientific Discovery and Logical Proof", in *Studies in the History and Method of Science* (Ed. C. Singer), vol. 1, (W. Dawson) 1917, p. 235.
[2] F. Waismann in *Contemporary British Philosophy, Third Series* (Ed. H. D. Lewis), 1956, p. 464. (Allen & Unwin).

pound packets of sugar and place one in each hand. Then I shut my eyes and try to guess which is the heavier. And suppose a psychologist insists that I *must* give an answer—I *must* say that this bag or that is the heavier, even though they feel equal in weight. I give an answer as demanded. What I say seems quite at random. And of course it *is* at random. If the experiment is conducted often enough, I will pronounce one particular bag or the other as the heavier an equal number of times.

But suppose sugar is withdrawn from one of the bags a little at a time. First a few grains, then a little more and yet more and more until, say, an ounce or an ounce and a half has been removed. After this has been done I am sure that one bag is the heavier. But when very little has been taken out, my decision still seems to be a matter of guesswork as before. It is impossible consciously to feel that one bag is one-thousandth part heavier than another.

Yet psychologists have found that when we guess in this way we guess rightly more often than wrongly. The two bags may *seem* to have identical weights, when we think about them, but in fact when we guess which is the heavier and think that our guess is just a guess and no more—in fact, then, our guess is surprisingly often right.[1] As Bates puts it: "As a task becomes more difficult, a point is reached at which the subject feels that every estimate he is making is a complete guess . . . it is found surprisingly, that within a particular range,

[1] For a popular account of work of this kind see H. T. Green, *New Scientist*, 2nd May, 1957. The same points might have been illustrated by older work on post-hypnotic suggestion.

if guessing is forced to continue, one is in fact correct far more often than would be expected by chance.[1]

Again, there is something influencing the way we choose. We think that we are guessing: we think that the senses have nothing to do with the way we answer. But in fact we are wrong. There is often a real physical cause for our choices. More often than not our seeming guesses are expressing objective truth about the world. We have gained this knowledge but reason has been by-passed.

Is Faith Guesswork?

But what has this to do with faith? There is no connection, surely, between the kind of "faith" we exercise when we guess and the faith about which religious people speak. When men say they have faith in God, are they merely guessing as when they guess which of two nearly identical weights is the heavier?

No, certainly not. But experiments of the kind we have considered do show, conclusively, that reason is not essential for knowledge. And if knowledge can enter our minds without reason—even though a psychologist thinks that it has come through our senses—then, on the face of it, it will be difficult to prove that knowledge may not come without by-passing our senses too, just as it may by-pass our reasoning mind.

Psychical Research and Knowledge

That this is no idle possibility seems to be shown by a mass of evidence which is steadily growing in our own day.

[1] J. A. V. Bates, *Jour. Instit. Elec. Engineers*, 1947, **94**, 298.

The belief that it is possible for one man to know what another man is thinking about, without physical communication between them, has been widely held since the dawn of history. The Bible tells the fascinating story of how Elisha knew the thoughts of the king of Syria so that, whenever the king of Syria made plans for an attack on Israel, the king of Israel had prior warning (2 Kings 6). In a lesser way nearly everyone has had the experience of talking to a friend who has suddenly said what they were about to say themselves. And most of us have heard stories of how, when loved ones were in danger, their friends at home have been aware of it in a strange and unaccountable way.

To frame foolproof experiments to confirm that this kind of experience does indeed happen, and that it cannot be accounted for in terms of scientific principles, has been one of the hardest tasks that has ever faced science. The more striking cases of telepathy are connected with death, sudden danger and intense need. To devise experiments—repeatable experiments— in which such factors are present is well-nigh impossible. Yet all the stories from the past seem to indicate that unless man's deepest emotions are involved telepathy will not work reliably.

Still, we must do the best we can. Since we *cannot* perform experiments which involve deep emotions, experiments of a trivial nature *must* be done instead. They may show nothing or they may show that telepathy is just beginning to operate even at this level.

Even if such experiments are successful, they certainly cannot be expected to give sensational results.

The method usually adopted is to take a pack of cards marked in special ways. Usually there are five different kinds of cards in a pack of 25, with five of each kind. We can imagine them numbered 1, 2, 3, 4, 5, 1, 2, 3, etc., though other markings are more often used. Suppose you take a pack of such cards, mixed at random, and pick up the cards one by one, while someone in another room guesses which one you have picked up. If chance, only, is operating he will be right just one-fifth of the times he guesses. And as a general rule this is, in fact, what we find. The average score is very close indeed to 20 per cent.

But every now and again it is discovered that someone has the power to guess above average. For short runs— a single run of 25 cards, for example—there would of course be nothing odd if someone guessed 7 or 10 correctly. But suppose he could keep this up for weeks on end: over tens of thousands of guesses, in fact—? Here mathematics enters the field. By applying mathematical formulae it is possible to tell fairly certainly whether the results can reasonably be attributed to chance or not. And it has been found in a number of such cases that the scores obtained are vastly higher than can reasonably be accounted for by chance.

By itself this might mean little. There might be some reason why the guessing was not at random. Suppose, for instance, that the cards had been arranged in the order 1, 2, 3, 4, 5, 1, 2, 3, 4, etc., and that the guesser also tended to go through the numbers in order. Then the guesser might get *all* the cards correct, but there would be no telepathy. Researches of this kind are full of pitfalls for the unwary, but competent workers know how to obtain reliable results, for the techniques have been worked out in a number of applied sciences and are therefore well known today. One obvious precaution is to arrange the cards in the first place in a way that can be tested for randomness. To sum the matter up, when every possible source of error has been allowed for, still the results persist.

Physical Communication Involved—?

Not only is chance out of the question, but careful work seems to indicate definitely that no method of physically communicating the results is operating. Experiments have been carried out between two people in different rooms of a large building, in towns miles apart and also thousands of miles apart. And still results are obtained.

If we send a physical ray from one place to another, the intensity of the ray, or whatever it may be, falls off with the distance. Light, sound and gravitation fall off as the square of the distance: the ability to pick up messages from a wireless transmitting station falls off directly as the distance. Yet nothing of this kind has ever been encountered in telepathy. It works as well over great distances as over small.

If we use physical means to send a message through space, we must turn the message first into a code and then, at the other end, we must decode our message. The code may consist of a language or of pictures, and these may have to be transformed again into electrical impulses, or an arrangement of ink marks on paper. The final code need not in any obvious way resemble the message that is being sent—the series of dots and dashes of Morse or the electromagnetic waves that represent a television picture are not immediately recognizable for what they are. At the other end complex equipment may recreate the speech or picture. This is finally decoded by someone who knows the language or artistic conventions. Here use may be made of the complex mechanisms of ear or eye in order that the message may be received by the brain, and much training is necessary before the mind can understand what the brain receives. Thus, people born blind who have later received their sight, do not recognise the picture world around them for the world which they knew by feeling. Similarly, words mean nothing unless we understand the language. If these complex processes break down at any point, no message is received.

Does telepathy work in this way? It scarcely seems so. No one has ever suggested that a code might be involved, far less a code that we must learn, nor has anyone who has received a telepathic message been aware that he was interpreting a code. Instead there is an impression of a direct awareness of knowledge which is independent of words. This, again, is difficult to understand if telepathy follows physical laws.

There is an odder circumstance still. It has been found

repeatedly that, in telepathy, the human mind can, to a limited extent, look into the future. Results may be very little above chance for the card that is being looked at, but surprisingly high for the one that is *going* to be looked at next. The mind of the person picking up the message seems able to look ahead and to know in some way not what is being thought of *now* by the person who is sending the message, but what *will* be thought of in a short interval of time. This upsets all laws of cause and effect. If I say, "I am thinking of such and such a card *because* so-and-so is thinking of it", I can at least say that one event is causally connected with another. But suppose the cause has not yet come into existence? What then? There would seem to be no answer here—yet the evidence that this occurs is very strong indeed[1].

Psychical Research and Rationalism

To the Rationalist these results have been extremely surprising—shatteringly so.[2] But not so to the Christian. Indeed, even the last result, if true, only means that a very limited ability to prophesy resides in many people today. The Christian will find no difficulty in thinking that a latent power, present perhaps in all of us, was

[1] The best general reference is S. G. Soal and F. Bateman, *Modern Experiments in Telepathy*, 1954. See also *Proceedings of the Society for Pyschical Research* and the *Journal of Parapsychology* for recent years. Also S. G. Soal and H. T. Bowden, *The Mind Readers*, 1959.

[2] In his book *Some Aspects of the Conflict between Science and Religion*, (Eddington Memorial Lecture, 1953), Professor H. H. Price who, in the past, has been no friend of Christianity, shows how the main tenets of religion have been powerfully supported by the results of psychical research in recent years.

used by God's Holy Spirit in ancient days when the prophets told what should happen in years to come. To say this, of course, explains nothing, nor must such a statement be allowed to detract from a study of the way in which the mind works. But at least it can be said that Christians have been much less prone to deny the existence of what they do not understand than have the adherents of materialistic science.

Science, then, has put on the map, so to speak, a good deal that was always held by Christians. But it is necessary to stress, once again, the seeming triviality of the type of experiment we have been discussing. In card guessing it is only very rarely—there are, however, a few such cases on record, if we may assume them to be reliable—that there is any complete certainty that a particular card has been guessed correctly. However, it has been found that the *feeling* of certainty that a guess is right *does* correlate with a correct guess. And the results obtained are quite compatible with the view that, in non-trivial cases when the emotions are aroused, telepathy can be something near 100 per cent. reliable.

But however this may be, let us take up the argument again from an earlier part of this chapter. Suppose I believe that someone else is thinking about a certain card. And suppose my belief is correct and that this particular "guess" is not the result of chance. How, I now ask, do I obtain this information? Not by reason. No amount of reasoning can tell me that I should choose one particular card rather than another. And this time not because my physical senses are telling me to choose this card and no other, as was the case in our earlier analogy.

It is evident, then, that the human mind can obtain information other than by reason and the senses. Though difficult to prove, numerous instances of visions of those dying or in danger make it highly probable, too, that such information *can* be reliable—even though (as with memory) we do not know how to discover whether it is reliable in any given instance.[1] The assumption that this cannot happen proves to be in conflict with fact.

[1] There is much evidence for this statement quite apart from psychical research—though it is often difficult to evaluate. Thus von Middendorf was baffled by the ability of natives to find their way home in Arctic snows without the slightest difficulty. Asked how they did it, they thought the questioner was silly. (see D. Katz, *Animals and Men*, 1937, p. 130). Similarly Charles Darwin (*Nature*, 1873, **7**, 418) cites the expedition of von Wrangell to N. Siberia in which the party passed "for a long distance through hummocky ice with incessant changes of direction and with no guide in the heavens or on the frozen sea", but again the natives had no difficulty in finding their way. "He, an experienced surveyor, and using a compass failed to do what these savages easily effected." Early Quaker saints had an uncanny power of knowing when and where people were ill or in danger and needed help (J. W. Graham, *Friends' Quarterly Journal*, 1933, Suppl. No. 18). "Calculating prodigies" may sense the answers to difficult arithmetical problems, immediately, infallibly and without calculation—J. Hadamard, *The Psychology of Invention in the Mathematical Field* (O.U.P.), 1945, p. 58. Such cases could be multiplied.

For a discussion of possible occurences of extra-sensory perception among primitive peoples, animals, etc., see the fascinating *CIBA Foundation Symposium on Extrasensory Perception* (Ed. G. E. W. Wolstenholme and E. C. P. Millar), 1956.

III

HOW SCIENCE ADVANCES

We have learned that knowledge may come without reason. But for many of us, at least, such knowledge—if ever we possess it—may seem hazy and unreal. It *seems* to be concerned with probability and guessing rather than with certainty. We tend to contrast it with the *certain* knowledge of science where reason supposedly reigns supreme. We tend to think that if science can make its amazing predictions by reason alone, then the knowledge that comes through reason is all we need.

Scientific Method—A Popular Conception

The plausibility of this argument depends upon a popular picture of the growth of science—a picture we must first examine.

Science, we are told, is systematized common sense. It starts with observation of the world around us. We reason about what we observe and suggest a hypothesis to explain it. We argue that if our hypothesis is right, a certain consequence will follow if we carry out such-and-such an experiment.

In the laboratory we put our hypothesis to the test and observe what happens. If results are as we expect, new experiments will be suggested and the hypothesis medicinal value of the salicylates (by far the most widely used of all synthetic drugs) to a positive belief in God or Providence. In 1763 Rev. Edward Stone introduced the willow bark as a cure for fever and, in 1874, MacLagan discovered that the use of salicin, again from the willow, is a specific remedy for rheumatic fever. Synthetic salicylates and aspirin were later tried, successfully, in place of the more costly willow extract. Stone states definitely that it was his belief that Providence had provided remedies for man's ailments where they were most needed which led him to try willow bark. MacLagan states that a similar line of reasoning led him to salicin.[1]

Discoverers have not always, of course, used the language of theology. Often they have felt that a truth was in some way hovering around in the deep recesses of the mind, a truth upon which they could not readily lay hold. Thus Einstein speaks of "the years of searching in the dark for a truth that one feels but cannot express."[2] Part of the difficulty seems to be that discoverers think, in the first place, without words. Galton describes how he would often have what he believed to be perfectly clear ideas but, when he tried to express them in words, only nonsensical words kept coming to his mind. If questioned, he would become confused. Maxwell, likewise, seems to have thought without words. His replies to questions were enig-

[1] E. Stone, *Phil. Trans. of the Royal Society*, 1763, 53, 195; T. J. MacLagan, *Lancet*, 1876 (i), 343 and *Rheumatism*, 1881, p. 192.
[2] A. Einstein, *Origins of the General Theory of Relativity* (Jackson, Glasgow), 1933.

will gradually become more refined and, in time, may become a respectable theory. If, on the other hand, things turn out unexpectedly, then a new hypothesis must be suggested. And so on, endlessly.[1]

> We dance round in a ring and suppose
> But the Secret sits in the middle and knows.
> (Robert Frost)

It is commonly claimed that the scientific method, described in some such way, supports Rationalism. In fact, Rationalists are often insistent that truth can be obtained only by the application of this rigorous scientific method. Thus one of their number—oddly enough he is also a scientist and his brilliant work belies his words—writes: "Scientific method . . . proceeds by a rigid logic to exclude any possible alternatives to its formal description . . . its conclusions follow inescapably from the observations which are its premises."[2]

The picture of the scientific method, as we have described it, is accurate enough, of course, *except for what it leaves out*. But it leaves out the most important feature of all. And it is safe to say that the prevalent idea that science can get along well enough today without the aid of faith is due to the prevalence of this half-truth about how scientific progress is achieved.

Unprejudiced investigation shows that in all radically new discoveries a non-rational element is supremely

[1] A varient of this view is that proposed by Karl Popper (*The Logic of Scientific Discovery*, Eng. Trans. 1959). The scientist puts forward a view and then tries to prove it false. Only those hypotheses which cannot be proved false survive.
[2] J. D. Bernal, in *Aspects of Dialectical Materialism*, 1934, p. 97.

important. Discovery often by-passes reason and involves faith, or something akin to faith—a fact which we shall consider with reference to both old and recent examples, for there has been no change with the passing of the years.

Theistic Faith in Science

Often the faith that has proved important has been, quite simply, faith in God. Kepler believed that a perfect God had made the universe perfectly. This idea had caused great difficulty in the past, for the planets did not move in circles, but after many years of labour Kepler was able to show that they moved in the equally "perfect" ellipses. Paracelsus was convinced that God had provided remedies in nature for the various diseases and this led him to his discovery of the use of minerals in medicine.[1]

Newton believed that in studying astronomy he would learn more about God, but it appears that when he found that his researches did not immediately aid him in theology and that they occasioned controversy, he lost interest in them. However, in writing his famous work, the *Principia*, theology was not neglected. "When I wrote my treatise about the system, I had an eye upon such principles as might work with considering men for the belief in a Deity and nothing can rejoice me more than to find it useful for that purpose," he wrote to Bentley. Pascal's interest in science and

[1] W. Pagel, *Isis*, 1938, **28**, 472.

mathematics also waned when he could not l theology and his brilliant genius was lost to the s world. For Robert Boyle, John Ray and many on the other hand, the feeling that science le nearer to God persisted through life and their in it did not flag.

Maupertuis argued that Divine perfection w opposed to any expenditure of energy by bodies beyond that necessary to get from one j another. It was this belief which led him to the pi of Least Action.[1] Balmer's desire to reveal "the orderliness" led him to the discovery of the series of spectral lines given by hydrogen in dis tubes.[2] Much of the early work on cosmolog embryology was inspired by Christian belie latter with a view to investigating the probl original sin! Such motives are not lacking even t

Ideas Hovering Around

In the field of pharmacology belief in God ha of great importance. Thus, we owe the discovery

[1] According to J. Jeans, [Sir] *Physics and Philosophy*, 1942, p.
[2] Cited by C. A. Coulson, *Science and Christian Belief*, 1955,
[3] This is freely admitted, for example, by A. L. Parsons, 1944, **154**, 707, in connection with his own work there des Purely anti-theistic bias also, at times, inspires new develop Thus H. Bondi almost admits that his theory of continuous crea matter in space is inspired by his desire to avoid belief in a Go created the Universe. When we accepted the conservation of i he says, "we had to believe in something outside science created matter at the beginning. But if we believed in the sys continuous creation . . . then it was the laws of science which supreme" (Report of a speech to the Rationalist Press Associ *Literary Guide*, 1950, p. 211).

matical and indirect when he was young and his attempts to lecture were often chaotic.[1]

In this we are reminded of the Kellogg boy Donald brought up with the ape Gua. When a tempting cookie (sweet) was suspended out of reach both knew, as if instinctively, that a nearby chair could help them. But at first the intuition hovered around in their minds before it became conscious.[2]

Such experiences are doubtless common. We are all familiar with the difficulties that arise when we try to remember a forgotten name. To begin with it seems to be at the fringe of consciousness—we seem to have remembered it, yet the actual word cannot be remembered sufficiently clearly for us to say it. Discoveries come in a similar way. Even when they flash into consciousness they may be lost as readily as the memory of a dream. "Many new ideas vanish as soon as they appear unless a particular effort is made to focus attention on them long enough to fix them in the memory."[3]

"Recording the Work of Another"

A most interesting feature of discovery is that it seems to come not from one's own mind but from outside. Rarely if ever does it seem to be the direct result of our reasoning. Helmholtz, in telling Lord

[1] R. E. M. Harding, *An Anatomy of Inspiration*, 2nd ed. (Cambridge), 1942, p. 90.
[2] W. N. and L. A. Kellogg, *The Ape and the Child*, 1933, p. 213.
[3] W. Platt and R. A. Baker, *Journal of Chemical Education*, 1931, **8**, 1969.

Kelvin of how he wrote his work on physiological optics, said: "I often had the impression that what I was putting down was not my own work at all, but I seemed to be recording the work of another." W. B. Cannon, Sir Frederick Gowland Hopkins[1] and many others have said the same.

A modern writer, describing the birth of a discovery says: "Suddenly the solution comes to him . . . He tries it and it works! Out of an almost infinite number of possible modes of attack, the right one has dawned upon him without effort—seemingly from Heaven!"[2]

"Beyond Reason"

When the intuition comes, scientists recognize at once that something beyond reason is involved. Irving Langmuir writes: "In almost every scientific problem which I have succeeded in solving . . . the final solution has come to my mind in a fraction of a second by a process which is not consciously one of reasoning."[3]

Gauss tried vainly for four years to solve a mathematical problem. "At last . . . I succeeded," he says, "not by dint of painful effort, but so to speak by the grace of God. As a sudden flash of light the enigma was solved. For my part I am not in a position to point to the thread which joins what I knew previously with

[1] W. B. Cannon, *The Way of an Investigator*, 1945. Hopkins, in conversation with colleagues (Dr Malcolm Dixon, *personal communication*).
[2] W. Platt, *Industrial and Engineering Chemistry*, 1929, **21**, 655.
[3] I. Langmuir, *Science*. 1943, **97**, 1.

what I succeeded in doing,"[1] and again, " I have my results but I do not yet know how I arrived at them".

Direct Effort Unavailing

Sudden illuminations rarely if ever come when one is working hard to obtain them. Conscious effort seems useless. A man may agonize in his thinking, but still the answer he seeks evades him. Yet when he relaxes and waits it often comes unexpectedly. "It is I think a general experience that new ideas about a subject come when one is not thinking about it at the time though one must have thought about it a good deal before," writes J. J. Thomson.[2]

Faraday, who believed with a passion that God who had made the universe must have made it interconnected as a single whole, with everything within it linked together, had worked ceaselessly to discover a connection between magnetism and electricity. He brought wires near to magnets time and time again— there was no electric current and no sign of interaction. He left the work for a holiday and, without effort, made the discovery of electromagnetic induction upon which so much of our civilization hangs today, immediately he returned to the work. "I have often observed that, by ceasing to think for some days of some very com-

[1] Quoted by M. Montmasson, *Invention and the Unconscious*, 1931, p. 77. This book contains a wealth of interesting information. Henri Poincaré describes similar experiences in his celebrated lecture to the Society of Psychology in Paris. (An English translation will be found in *Foundations of Science*, 1913, p. 387).

[2] J. J. Thomson, *Recollections and Reflections*, 1936, p. 82.

plicated question, it became quite easy to me when I came to consider it afresh," writes Laplace.[1]

The following are two further quotations from the Platt and Baker questionnaire which bear out the same point.

> Decided to abandon work . . . and then on the following day when occupied in work of an entirely different type, an idea came to my mind as suddenly as a flash of lightning and it was the solution.
>
> One Sunday in church the correct principle came like a flash as the preacher was announcing the text.[2]

In Dreams

Sometimes a discovery is born not in the waking life at all but in dreams or in a dreamy state of consciousness. Cannon reminds us of how Otto Loewi, of the University of Graz, was awakened one night by a brilliant idea. He scribbled a note about it and slept again. The whole of the next day he struggled to read his own writing, or at least remember his dream—but in vain. The following night the same idea came and again he awoke. He made careful notes this time and the following day performed an epoch-making experiment in physiology, showing for the first time that chemical substances are involved in the triggering

[1] Montmasson, *op. cit.* p. 72.
[2] For further instances see Platt and Baker, *loc. cit.*; A. L. Porterfield's *Creative Factors in Scientific Research*, 1941, esp. p. 94; W. B. Cannon, *The Way of an Investigator*, N.Y., 1945; Montmasson, *op. cit.*; *Creativity and its Cultivation*, Ed. H. H. Anderson (Interdisciplinary Symposia on Creativity, Michigan University) (Harpers), 1959; etc.

off of nerve impulses to muscles.[1] Cannon himself records that his first awareness of a number of his own ideas came immediately after he had awaked from sleep during the night hours.

We read of how Goodyear worked tirelessly to overcome the stickiness of rubber in hot weather, but without success. But one night he dreamed that a man came and told him to add sulphur. He had tried this before without success and had long ago abandoned the use of this material. But he tried again and immediately discovered how to vulcanize rubber.[2]

It was in a dream also that Alfred Werner first learned the theory of co-ordination for which his name is honoured. It was in a half-awake, half-asleep state that Mendeleev in 1869 first had a vision of the arrangement of the chemical elements according to his periodic law. W. H. Rivers, the psychologist, likewise claimed that the ideas which he valued most came to him in a similar half-dozing condition. Every schoolboy who learns organic chemistry knows how Kekulé made his two great discoveries upon which organic chemistry rests—the structure theory and the formula for benzene —the first when he dozed on a bus late at night, the second years later when he dozed by the fireside. In both cases he saw visions of atoms gambolling before his eyes and was able to watch how they arranged themselves.

[1] W. B. Cannon, *op. cit.*, p. 60.
[2] See R. W. Lunn, *Industrial and Engineering Chemistry*, 1939, 31, 1191.

Logic—An Enemy

These and thousands of similar examples show that discovery comes when the reasoning mind is asleep—when the mind is not working logically but, as it were, freely, so that new ideas which enter have a chance to become accepted before they are rudely brushed aside by the critical intellect. It is not a logical mind that the discoverer needs: at the moment of discovery logic is his enemy.

Sometimes, however, reasoning proves most valuable—but often it is not sound logical reasoning. It may happen, for example, that a crude analogy (crude, that is to say, by the standards of our critical minds) is the only type of reasoning available to an inventor.

Goodyear used to argue that since leather could be tanned and iron was improved by adding carbon, there must be some way to "tan" rubber also.[1] This argument sustained his faith during his prolonged researches until, at last, he succeeded. Paul Ehrlich argued that since dyes selectively stain bacteria, poisonous chemical substances could be prepared which would selectively attach themselves to parasites and kill them without hurting the host. Again his faith, supported by this somewhat crude argument which has turned out in many instances to be wrong (chemotherapeutic drugs are not always attached to bacteria in the way he supposed), supported Ehrlich through all but insuperable difficulties, years of failure and constant admoni-

[1] See R. W. Lunn, *loc. cit.*

tion from friends to abandon the work, until, at last, success crowned his efforts.[1]

Marconi, it is said, gazed one day at a distant horizon. He thought of how the human mind knew no barriers but could bridge every distance, even reaching to God in meditation and prayer. In a flash the idea came to him that Hertzian waves, also, might overcome the obstacles of space. Before long he was pioneering in wireless.[2]

Repeated Return in Thought

Discoverers seem to be agreed that truth only comes if the mind keeps returning to a problem again and again. Edison tells how he would keep many lines of thought going simultaneously, dropping each one in turn when difficulties arose and continuing with another so as not to waste time, and then coming back to the abandoned ones over and over again.[3] Alfred Nobel writes: "I worked intermittently; I left a matter alone for a time and then took it up again. I work like that fairly often, but I shall always return to anything of which I have the feeling that I shall succeed with it in the end"[4] Newton, Faraday and many others worked on the same principle.

Conviction

A characteristic of discovery is that it brings conviction with it. The sudden idea not only illuminates problems which have proved puzzling for a long time

[1] M. Marquardt, *Paul Ehrlich*, 1949.
[2] *Religious Digest*, 1945, Quoted, *Dawn*, 1945, **22**, 101.
[3] *Science News Letter*, 9th Feb. 1957.
[4] H. E. Pauli, *Alfred Nobel—Dynamite King—Architect of Peace*, 1947, p. 138.

but illuminates them in such a way that doubt seems impossible. "It is remarkable that when ideas come in this way", writes J. J. Thomson, "they carry conviction with them and depose without a struggle ideas which previously had seemed not unsatisfactory." Poincaré likewise speaks of "the absolute conviction which accompanies the inspiration". In most cases when he had this conviction the idea proved sound, but this was not always the case with those ideas which came when he was asleep or in a sleepy state of mind.

Of those who replied to the Platt and Baker questionnaire, 7 per cent. stated that they had never known intuitions which came with a sense of certainty to prove wrong. Though this percentage is low, it seems that many of the greatest discoveries have been accompanied by a sense of certainty. F. Joliot records that the proof of uranium fission came with certainty.[1] Charles Nicolle knew in a flash how typhus was transmitted—to please the scientific world he had to confirm his hypothesis by experimentation, but in doing so experienced "strange sentiments of the pointlessness of any demonstration, of complete detachment of the mind and of wearisome boredom".[2]

Joy

Discovery is also characterized by the intense joy to which it gives rise. This joy is often described as being so great that no words are able to describe it.

[1] Conversation with Hadamard mentioned by R. Taton, *Reason and Chance in Scientific Discovery* (Hutchinson), 1957, p. 41.
[2] Chas. Nicolle, *Biologie de l'Invention*, Paris, 1932.

When for the first time Davy saw the alkali metals as silver balls floating in his melt, he is said to have literally danced for joy. Faraday exhibited boyish glee with each discovery that he made. Harvey declared that the pains of discovery are amply compensated for by the "pleasures of discovery". A. R. Wallace caught a new species of butterfly and was at once overwhelmed with joy—but his joy was more than he could bear: "I had a headache for the rest of the day." Lister, in describing his first use of antiseptic ligatures to a friend, said: "I don't think any case excited me so much." Bell was delighted with his first telephone and Edison with his phonograph. After the first Atlantic cable was laid, Kelvin was "evidently in a state of enjoyment so intense as almost to absorb the whole soul and create absence of mind". Scheele, the discoverer of chlorine, exclaimed: "Oh, how happy I am . . . there is no delight like that which comes from discovery." Galileo, amazed at what he saw through his telescope, said: "Being infinitely amazed thereat, so do I give infinite thanks to God who has pleased to make me the first observer of marvellous things unrevealed to bygone ages." Kepler wrote of what he considered to be his greatest discovery: "The intense pleasure I have received from this discovery can never be told in words." Pasteur says: "When you have at last arrived at certainty, your joy is one of the greatest that can ever be felt by a human soul." And Claude Bernard says: "The joy of discovery is certainly the loveliest that the mind of man can ever feel," but insists that, "those who do not know the torment

35

of the unknown can never have the joy of discovery".[1]

These and many other stories and quotations of like kind are well enough known. In Frazer-Harris's words: "The joy of scientific discovery is one of the most exalted human emotions." In former ages thoughtful people looked forward with intense longing to the joy that would come when more was known about nature. We may close this chapter with the words of Job of Edessa, who flourished at Baghdad in the early ninth century:

> If we do rejoice when we acquire the knowledge of the building of houses how much more shall we experience an ineffable joy when we shall have acquired a perfect knowledge of the composition of this world, the greatness of the heavens and its nature, the right size and nature of the sun, moon and stars, the knowledge of the composition and differentiation of each species (of created things), the union of the soul with the body and of all the world? Will it not be a wonderful joy, of which we have no experience here, and which does not fall under any of the senses? Since, however, we have not experienced it, we cannot possibly describe it.[2]

[1] Most of these quotations are taken from Frazer-Harris's lecture to the British Association (see *Nature*, 1936, **138**, 498), and the last three from W. I. B. Beveridge's valuable book, *The Art of Scientific Investigation* (Heinemann), 2nd ed., 1953, in which much useful information will be found. The quotation from Galileo is taken from J. G. Crowther, *The Social Relations of Science*, 1941, p. 317.

[2] Job of Edessa, *Book of Treasures*, trans. from Syriac by A. Mingana (A.D. 817), (Cambridge), 1935, p. 285.

IV

THE HUNCH
Encouragements and Hindrances

BEFORE leaving the subject of the scientific inspiration or "hunch", as it is commonly called, something must be said about the conditions which help or hinder discovery.

Modern study, including questionnaires and examination of the circumstances of thousands of hunches have revealed a number of interesting points about them.

Aids to Discovery

As we have already noted, ideas come chiefly when the critical judgment is relaxed, generally after a period of intense effort followed by inactivity.

Sometimes discussion with fellow scientists has proved helpful, but only when conducted in a spirit of peacefulness and friendliness. Ideas rarely if ever come during the course of an argument conducted in a spirit of criticism. Sometimes, however, the presence of other people is fatal. One man recorded: "No hunch has ever come to me in the presence of any other person." It seems to be a universal experience that petty irritation, noise, a life of routine, depression, anger, and above all worry, are fatal to inspiration.

As helps towards the peaceful disposition that is necessary, music and listening to sermons have often been cited. But of greater help than anything, perhaps, is natural scenery. Bunsen, Helmholtz, Van't Hoff, Ostwald, Willstätter, Hans Spemann and many others have testified to its value. The beauty of scenery helps to free the mind of trivial worries and to make it restful and uncritical. It is then, as Helmholtz put it: that ideas may come suddenly "as though inspired".

The Danger of Knowledge

The need to relax the critical judgment—to become as a little child, forgetful of the knowledge one has so painfully acquired, is, doubtless, the most important condition of all. Stories are told of how men, on the very brink of great discoveries, have let their knowledge interfere at the last moment. On 8th May 1795 Lalande, a highly trained French astronomer, saw a new star. Two days later he saw it again, but noted that the position had shifted. He crossed out the first position in his record and marked the second as doubtful—though in fact he had seen the then unknown planet Neptune.[1]

Sir Oliver Lodge used to tell the story of a man who, on finding that some photographic plates which were in a box standing near a vacuum tube became fogged, was so annoyed with this disturbance to his experiments

[1] W. M. Smart, *Nature*, 1946, **158**, 648.

that in future he kept the plates in another place. In this way an earlier discovery of X-rays was missed.[1] If the mind is not fresh and child-like, it is easy to fail to see the significance of the obvious.

It is in this connection, particularly, that the role of accidents enters our discussion. If the mind is critical, the accidental discovery, even of a new planet, is written off as a mistaken observation.[2]

A scientist must be prepared to consider an inspiration seriously. He must not turn it aside just because it is illogical in its first beginnings. At a later stage, of course, the reason must be used and proves invaluable. It is then that the "scientific method" as we have described it, becomes important. We do not belittle reason when we realize that reason must, in the first place, build on faith.

To adopt an attitude which is for ever dissecting and criticizing is, then, worse than useless. Our aim must always be to find out what the facts, *taken as a whole*, are trying to tell us. The relationship between them, even when we have found it, will certainly not be the *whole* truth. There may be complicating factors about which we shall know nothing for years to come and these will probably mean that some of the facts will not fit neatly into the correct theory after the latter has been discovered. This is inevitable. It means that it will be

[1] *Nature*, 1943, **151**, 55.
[2] Many of the so-called accidents which have led to great discoveries, as for example the "accident" that led to the discovery of penicillin, occurred again and again before their significance was appreciated. On this subject see Beveridge, *op. cit.*

necessary to overlook, for the time being, *some* of the facts as a necessary condition for thinking at all. If we fail to realize this point, we may place a considerable barrier in the path of discovery.

Overlooking Facts

Science offers many illustrations of these points. Prout's theory of the unity of matter, though suggested by the facts taken as whole, could easily be made to look impossible if attention was directed upon the details which seemed to be at variance with it. Copernicus had to ignore the fact that in his day stellar parallax had never been observed, though astronomers had sought it for centuries, otherwise he could never have established his theory of the rotation of the earth round the sun. Newton had to ignore what was considered to be a well-established fact in his day—the fact that motion always dies down of itself—before he could discover his laws of motion. Kekulé had to ignore the existence of carbon monoxide before he could establish his theory of the quadrivalency of carbon. Similarly, atomic physicists had to ignore the repulsion of like charges before they could develop the theory of the structure of the cores of atoms. Of Tamm and Frank's explanation (1937) of Cerenkov radiation it is said: "The theory was not very difficult but the concept of material bodies not being able to move faster than the speed of light was by then so ingrained that it required tremendous originality to break away from it."[1]

[1] T. Margerison in *New Scientist*, 1958, p. 1216.

Similar examples could probably be furnished from every branch of science.

This point is of great importance in connection with religious faith. If we approach the Bible looking for mistakes and contradictions, or if we lose sight of the grandeur and wonder of creation because we are bent upon seeing, say, the existence of evil out of due perspective, it may be for ever impossible for us to see the wood for the trees.

At this point we encounter a serious difficulty. Is it honest to ignore what does not fit in with our theory? Will our ideas be of any value at all if we approach the facts whilst willing to overlook what we do not like?

There are two issues here which must not be confused. Truth comes to our minds as a flash of light when we see suddenly what was previously hidden from us. But the new perception comes only when our minds are non-critical and receptive—as we have noted, it may come even in our dreams. The state of mind in which truth is first revealed to us is, then, an alogical one. If we refuse to accept it as such we set up a barrier which will prevent discovery. Here, then, there is no question of honesty or dishonesty. No one demands that we should be logical and intellectually consistent in our dreams!

Afterwards, of course, when a truth has discovered itself to us, the situation is different. Although some apparent intuitions may prove to be the veriest nonsense quickly to be disposed of, yet we must take great care not to throw away a pearl because it does not fit in with our preconceived notions of what it ought to look like.

Danger of Ignoring Facts

Yet, having said this, it is still possible to accept truth in such a way that dishonesty is encouraged. We may allow the truth to hide from us those facts which it fails to explain.

Indeed, the more brilliantly the new theory illuminates our minds, the greater will be the risk that we shall blind ourselves to the existence of the facts which we had to overlook in order that we should discover the theory at all. We are all familiar with the way in which some religious people, who have an axe to grind, will discover in the Bible certain passages which seem to support their point of view, but will be oblivious to the existence of other passages because they are hard to reconcile with the views they hold.

The story of science abounds with similar examples. Before the days of Darwin, scientists were deeply impressed by the amazing way in which the properties of the chemical elements seemed to be in line with the requirements of life. When Darwin and Wallace argued that species could have become adapted to their environment by natural selection and that this was the mechanism of evolution, the fact that chemical atoms did not alter in accordance with the law of natural selection was generally overlooked! After many years Lawrence Henderson again drew attention to the facts which had so largely been forgotten.

42

Chemistry affords instances of a similar kind. Thus, around 1900 Thiele proved conclusively that the facts of carbon chemistry cannot be explained, only, in terms of the traditional single, double and triple bonds. He produced evidence for half bonds in addition— "partial valencies", as he called them. Some decades later the bonds of chemistry were explained in terms of electrons—two electrons made a single bond, four a double bond, and six a triple bond. Half bonds now had no meaning, for electrons were arranged in pairs. Thiele was forgotton and his experiments ignored. Yet he was right, and more modern theories account for his discoveries.

Probably all branches of science could furnish similar examples. "The brighter the light that a new theory sheds on its proper field, the darker, and the more distorting, the shadows in which it submerges the experience which lies around the borders of its true scope," writes Polanyi.[1] If, then, Christians have sometimes been unwilling to think about facts difficult to reconcile with their faith, we need not be surprised. It is a failure to which all men are prone, scientists included.

Facing the Unpalatable

Yet the facts we have been discussing presents a challenge to be faced. If we have received faith—be it scientific or religious is no matter—what should be our attitude towards facts which cannot easily be reconciled with what we believe?

[1] M. Polanyi, *Nature*, 1942, **149**, 103.

A possible answer is as follows. Our knowledge of the universe, though large by our standards, is almost infinitely small. We may, with God's help, be able to understand important points and to make generalizations, but we can scarcely hope to understand all the complicating factors which will create apparent exceptions to the laws we have discovered. Nevertheless, some of these exceptions may be the preludes to future discovery. We must, therefore, keep them in mind. We must reconcile ourselves, perhaps for ever, to holding seemingly irreconcilable facts—in much the same way as theoretical physicists are forced to believe that light is both like a wave and like a particle.

We may hold that one day what now seems irreconcilable will be seen to be due to complicating factors, but we must not let our theory blind us to the existence of the facts which do not fit in.

Though Christians have failed at times, the record of Christianity in this respect is good. Christians have always held that when God looked upon the world He had made, He pronounced it good. But this belief has never blinded them, down the ages, to the existence of evil. As to the nature of that evil, they profess to know very little—it has always been held that it is a complicating factor and that one day, perhaps in an age to come, we shall understand what now seems incongruous. This attitude is scientific and sensible. The notion that we should expect, in the course of a mere lifetime, to integrate our minds to so great an extent that all our knowledge will seem connected and self-consistent, is

44

born of intellectual pride. Young archangels, perhaps, might hope to realize this very possibility, but hardly men.

It is customary to smile at the story of the parson who, in the course of a sermon, said: "And now, my friends, we encounter a difficulty. Let us look it straight in the face and pass on." But he did the right thing: he was honest. New light can come if difficulties are faced in this way, but none at all if casuistry is used to remove difficulties from sight.

Age-old Controversies

Another great hindrance to discovery is the feeling that a subject is age-old and stale. If the same problems have been faced and the same hypotheses repeatedly advanced over thousands of years—where is the incentive to throw new light upon a problem? The motions of the stars had been discussed endlessly for two thousand years at least, many great intellects devoting their energies to the problem, but without success. A small minority had, perhaps, held the heliocentric theory from the days of Aristarchus in ancient Greece and onwards, but it seemed impossible that a proof of it would ever be forthcoming. Yet Copernicus was undeterred: he reinterpreted the facts in a new way and laid the foundations for a reform in astronomy.

It was the same in chemistry. Controversy between believers and disbelievers in atoms had gone on inconclusively for thousands of years, but, in the seventeenth century, atomism became generally accepted—

as yet on inadequate and slender grounds—and progress became more rapid.

The history of science appears to show that it is unwise and hampering to refuse to look at well-known facts with the help of a new insight. Indeed, many discoveries come in this very way. Speaking of new physical theories and the new predictions that have been made in modern physics, Frenkel says: "These predictions were in almost every case the outcome of a theory which aimed, not at forecasting new, but at explaining old, phenomena."[1]

In theology, too, the same difficulty is often felt. Religious controversy is as ancient as astronomical or atomic controversy; but that, in itself, is no hindrance to new insights and understandings today.

Intensity

Another obstacle in the path of discovery arises from laziness or from inability or unwillingness to work with sufficient intensity. We are apt to imagine that discovery is like gardening or the ironing of clothes— work at half the speed and at the end of the day half the work is done. It is not so. "Problems are not solved more slowly by easier going: rather they are not solved at all unless the attack reaches a certain intensity."[2] The merchantman seeking goodly pearls cannot obtain the pearl on which he has set his heart until he has

---

[1] J. Frenkel, *Nature*, 1944, **154**, 417.
[2] H. S. Hatfield. *Proc. Instit. Mechanical Engineers*, 1934, **126**, 21. The Symposium of which Hatfield's paper formed a part is a valuable source reference. See also C. Nicolle, *op. cit.*

sold all that he has (Matt. 13.45-46). Or again, there may be a temptation to suppose that *any* time will do. But in fact it will not. The sudden hunch brings with it, not infrequently, the energy and enthusiasm necessary for the task. If there is delay, the opportunity is lost. It may be impossible, at a later date, to recapture the necesssary mood. In addition, insights are rarely given in words and so are easily lost if we fail to develop them at the time they come.

V

FAITH AND HYPOTHESIS

At this point it may seem that an obvious difference between religious faith and the non-rational element in scientific discovery has been insufficiently considered. The scientist is trained to submit each new hypothesis to the test of experiment and observation. If the hypothesis is wrong, then, no matter how attractive it may seem, it must be abandoned for another which accords better with experience. But can a religious person speak of God as a hypothesis? Can he experiment on the truth of Christianity? Is he prepared to believe in God today but change his opinion tomorrow if fresh evidence runs contrary? Are the historic creeds mere lists of hypotheses? To ask these questions is surely to answer them. The gulf between the scientific attitude and religious faith could scarcely be more impressive.

Hypothesis and Faith

So, at least, it is often argued. But a fallacy lurks in the reasoning. Science, as we have noted, requires faith for its progress as well as theories and hypotheses. And religion requires theories and hypotheses as well as faith. To compare the hypotheses of one with the faith of the other is to court confusion.

Many of the examples cited in Chapter 3 illustrate the difference between strong faith on the one hand and the tentative hypothesis on the other. The guiding ideas that motivated van Helmont, Kepler, Faraday, Maupertuis, Balmer, Ehrlich and others were not held one day and abandoned the next. They did not depend upon the results of experiments to confirm or disprove them. If the facts seemed contrary, it was a challenge to faith—a challenge tackled in a spirit of adventure and determination.

Take Faraday, for instance. By faith he believed in the unity of nature. He *knew* that gravity and electricity were in some way connected. Repeated efforts to find the connection were unavailing. Yet, in the 24th series of his *Experimental Researches*, communicated to the Royal Society in 1850, he closes with the words: "Here end my trials for the present. The results are negative; but they do not shake my strong feelings of the existence of a relation between gravity and electricity." Ten years later, "he says the same thing, almost in the same words, in the very last paper he wrote".[1] A century has passed and we are still little if any nearer to discovering the relation he sought—but most physical scientists would probably agree that Faraday's "strong feeling" was right.

Faith of a similar kind enters into much modern investigation of the highest order. Many scientists have a deep-rooted faith in the essential truth of the laws of

[1] Faraday, *Life and Letters*, 1870, vol. II, p. 253.

thermodynamics. In the early days of Rutherford's career it was found that radium maintains a temperature higher than that of its surroundings. Here, it seemed to some, was convincing proof that one or other of the first two laws of thermodynamics was wrong after all. Either energy was in process of creation contrary to the first law or, more likely, radium makes use of the heat in the surrounding air, contrary to the second. But Rutherford would have none of it. He continued his work on the assumption that the laws were right and that some new effect was involved.[1] Again, C. G. Darwin tells us how, in a letter to *Nature*, someone drew attention to an apparent contradiction in the quantum theory. Darwin's attitude is instructive: "One's immediate feeling was that the idea must be wrong (as indeed it proved to be), but . . . I did not care much whether it was right or wrong, because the quantum theory must be right anyhow."[2] Narrow-minded? A failure to be reasonable? Who will say it?

Individual Faith

Or there may be positive faith that it is destined for *me* to achieve some discovery or invention. From the

[1] *Background to Modern Science* (Eds. J. Needham and W. Pagel.) p. 58. Rutherford speaks of "the prevailing idea that radium had a peculiar property of acting as a thermodynamic engine using heat from the air". Similarly Sir H. Dale tells us that when Strutt (later Lord Rayleigh) described Becquerel's discovery of penetrating rays from uranium, a member of the scientific society at Cambridge which he had addressed said: "Why, Strutt, it would violate the law of conservation of energy!"—*Brit. med. J.*, 1948 (ii), 451 (4th Sept.).
[2] C. G. Darwin [Sir], *Reports, British Association* (Cambridge), 1938. 21.

days of World War I and onwards Sir Alexander
Fleming was convinced that a chemical could be found
with which to fight bacterial infection without damaging
tissues, but not till years after did he become a pioneer
in the antibiotic field.[1] Whinfield, the discoverer of
Terylene, writes: "The idea of one day discovering a
synthetic fibre had become fixed in my mind and I
returned to it again and again during the next 18 years."
In 1940 success came "in, as it were, a single bound".[2]
A faith which can be nurtured for so many years is not
of the kind that can be proved or disproved as a result
of a few experiments in the laboratory.

Or take cancer research. Those who work in this
field believe that the problem of finding a cure can be
solved. The belief is not a hypothesis or theory to be
judged by how experiments happen to turn out.
Otherwise, in view of the immense effort already
expended, we might be told that the theory must be
abandoned and further research given up.[3]

---

[1] A. Maurois, *The Life of Sir Alexander Fleming*, 1959.

[2] *Chemistry and Industry Review*, 1951, 346 (5th May).

[3] The present writer can give further, though relatively trivial,
examples from his own limited experience. The conviction that I would
or could discover how to construct a rotary pump by which fluid could
be pumped in small quantities and the exact volume read on a scale
came around 1942. In the years that followed I returned to the problem
scores of times but could see no way to achieve this result. The idea of
the "rotary burette" embodied in *British Patent* 783,884 came suddenly,
apparently in answer to prayer, during a leisurely walk in 1954. It did
not seem to come from my own mind at all: the vision of how to make the
apparatus seemed like a direct revelation but was accompanied with no
emotion at the time. A strong conviction that it would be possible to use
dithiol as a general reagent for metals in analytical chemistry grew
slowly from about 1937 onwards. Again, I returned to the problem
time and time again only to retreat each time baffled by the difficulties.
But in the end these difficulties were solved quite simply one by one

It may be answered, of course, that *eventually* experiment or experience will decide whether a theory is right, even though the vindication may not be within the lifetime of the experimenter. This may well be so, but is hardly to the point. Men like Faraday needed faith to inspire them in their work—they could not wait until after they were dead in order to be sure that their hypotheses were true. The parallel with religious faith is obvious enough. Again, the final vindication will come after we are dead. The Christian predicts certain verifiable consequences if his faith is correct—a resurrection and a day of judgment, for instance. But religious faith is needed here and now—we cannot wait till after we are dead to find whether the predictions come true.

Basic Elements of Faith in Science

At this point is may be helpful to think of some of the basic elements of faith which are involved in scientific work.[1] Our list will not, of course, exhaust the element of faith in science, for much scientific work is individualistic. Like Einstein, the individual worker may know

---

(*Analyst*, 1957-59, *passim.*). A definite faith that the capstan (torque amplifier) principle would have applications in chemistry led, after some ten years, to the publication of several papers (for example, *Jour. Soc. Chem. Ind.*, 1940, **59**, 216). It may be added that this book is the result of faith. For twenty-five years I collected material, off and on, believing that a book would one day be possible. A few ideas came in 1934 (*Contemporary Review*, 1934, **146**, 699), but I could get no further, despite repeated efforts. Then, quite suddenly, in the summer of 1956, the ideas took shape. Other work was set aside and within ten days a first draft was written.

[1] For a suggested scientific creed see "Symposium on the Presuppositions of Science", *Trans. Victoria Institute*, 1956, **88**, 63.

intuitively what he is about to discover and, as a result of faith, may sense the truth before he can describe it in words.

Firstly, then, with regard to the *motive* that underlies research. Most writers declare that curiosity is the chief motive for scientific research. It would seem clear that this is not so. If I am curious, why do I not attempt to read and learn all the science that has already been discovered, at least in my own subject? Curiosity can be satiated much more rapidly this way than by exploring a new field where progress is bound to be slow. There would seem to be no answer to this question, if the curiosity theory is right. But in fact it is wrong. The motive for research lies in the fact that the research worker longs, above all else, to *realize* his own faith. It is this realization that gives satisfaction and joy. It is the looking forward to the end of the journey which supplies the emotion which keeps the research worker at his bench. Faith is essential to the venture of research.

Secondly, there can be little headway made in science unless those who tread her paths believe that there is an absolute difference between truth and error and that it is man's duty to discover and accept truth. Here a strong element of faith is obviously involved—it is hard enough to express in logical language precisely what such terms as "truth" and "error" mean, and no one supposes that it is possible to prove that a man *ought* to seek one rather than the other.

It must be admitted that, in recent years, this principle

53

has sometimes been challenged.[1] It is claimed that science is not out to discover truth, its object being only to connect our experiences with one another (to "correlate sense-data"—to use the usual jargon). However, it is difficult, at times, not to suspect that those who make these claims are doing so with their tongues in their cheeks. Do they seriously contend that discoveries, say, in anatomy, or theories about the past history of our planet, are mental constructs only which have no necessary connection with a real world of nature? Deny that man evolved from animals and they are soon up in arms!

It would take us too far afield to continue this discussion here—but at least, no one will challenge the statement that science has reached its present position as a result of the so-called "older" view. This view is, of course, still widely accepted.

Again, it is assumed in all scientific work that the universe must be taken seriously. It is not a hoax or a nightmare. This may seem obvious enough, yet we cannot *prove* that what happens to us when we are awake is to be taken any more seriously than what seems to happen when we are asleep. In our dreams we see and feel, yet we make no attempt to create a body of science relating to our dream world. There are no rational grounds why we should not attempt to do so.

[1] For the most part, however, not by scientists but by philosophers, notably the logical positivists. For an interesting but very unsatisfying attempt by a scientist to maintain this point of view, see W. H. George, *The Scientist in Action*, 1935.

In the seventeenth century Descartes felt this to be a very real difficulty. He came to the conclusion that unless a man trusts in God he can never be certain that the world is as it seems to be. Only when you believe in a perfect and righteous God can you trust Him not to deceive you. Butterfield thus summarizes Descartes' view: "Without Him (God) a man could not trust in anything, could not believe in a geometrical proposition, for He was the guarantee that everything was not an illusion, the senses not a complete hoax, and life not a mere nightmare."[1]

Again, without proof, scientists accept the view that other people than themselves experience the world much as they do. Philosophers have often played with the view that this may not be so: but it is essential to science.

Again, scientists hold that the human mind is made in such a way that it is capable of understanding the universe—or at least enough of it to make science a worth-while task unendingly. In our day when we can see the results of scientific study around us on every side and the benefits it has bestowed upon man, such a belief is natural enough. But it was not always so. In earlier days a large element of faith was needed.

Yet again, there is a general belief in the unity of nature—a belief which seems to have arisen from the Christian view that one God made the universe. This view had never seemed compelling in cultural surroundings where many gods were worshipped. If one part of the universe had been made by one god and another by

[1] H. Butterfield, *Origins of Modern Science*, 1949, p. 99.

another, there would be no reason to expect that the laws which apply on earth would apply, also, to the stars. The Greek notion that everything beyond the orb of the moon was of a different nature to that on earth held sway until the modern era.

Armchair Thinking

Another important scientific belief is that one cannot, simply by thinking, construct a model of the universe. This is a relatively recent idea and it is due, once again, to the influence of Christianity on the Western world. We are apt to take it for granted, yet the ancient Greeks, for example, supposed that you could sit in an armchair and learn your science by meditating. You had but to work out logically how certain principles would apply throughout the universe, and all knowledge was yours. This attitude, to a great extent, permeated the Middle Ages, but it was derived, not from Christianity, but as a heritage from the Greeks. The contrast between our own point of view and that of the ancients could not be more forcefully brought home than by comparing our present views with those of Aristotle as illustrated by the following passage:

> "We must not fail to keep in mind the length of time and multitude of years in which these things, if they had been good, would certainly not have remained unknown; for almost everything has been found out, though in some cases what is known has not been systematised, and in other cases men do not make use of the knowledge which they have."[1]

[1] Aristotle *Politics*, II, 1264a, 1-5.

But when we contrast the philosophy of Aristotle with that of our day, we must not overlook the equally striking contrast with the Bible. Much of the Book of Job is concerned to show how infinitesimal is man's knowledge and the same thought arises repeatedly in the Old and New Testaments. The Bible inculcates a humility that was generally out of place in the pagan world but is wholly in keeping with modern science. Despite all the research that has been conducted, almost every development in science throws into relief some new field of knowledge virtually unexplored.

The ancients were not the only people to imagine that they knew most of what there is to know. In the hey-day of Rationalism, at the end of the nineteenth century, it was common for professors of physics to imagine that the end of their science was in sight. All they hoped to do in future years was to refine their measurements, taking them to another place of decimals. Clerk-Maxwell's comment left no doubt as to the Christian attitude: "We have no right to think thus of the unsearchable riches of creation."[1]

Today we think of science as an infinite quest. Our attitude appears to have arisen historically out of the Christian view that God is Creator. The Greeks, natur-ally enough, held no such notion since they supposed that an inferior spirit or *demiurge* had made the world. But a universe made by a God, infinite in power and knowledge, is likely to be for ever beyond the under-

---

[1] From the *Inaugural Lecture* at Cambridge, 1871. Quoted in *Life*, p. 356.

standing of man. Science is an unending task. The joy of discovery will never be denied to future generations. Already this belief is becoming enshrined as a part of the unwritten faith of science.

Creeds and Attitudes

In the foregoing paragraphs we have pictured the activity of science as dependent upon a set of beliefs. We have imagined a *creed* of science. Though this is legitimate enough, it is certainly unconventional. Scientists do not generally think in these terms—in starting an experiment they do not say, "Now, what does my creed say about it?" When they consider such matters they usually prefer to think of their *attitude*, rather than their *belief*. They possess an attitude towards nature—an attitude of trust (nature is not fooling them), an attitude of objectivity towards experience and knowledge (others experience the world as they do and reason similarly), and so on. Analysing this attitude we conclude, rightly enough, that it is based upon a creed—a set of beliefs—but the creed need not be conscious.

Here again the analogy with religion is remarkably close. It has often been pointed out that religious creeds may, at least for the most part, be thought of as rather sophisticated summaries of the ways in which Christians live—of their attitude to God and His Universe. When Christians begin to think about their religion it is this attitude rather than a set of fixed beliefs which first comes to their minds.

58

Changes in the Pattern of Faith

Without beliefs or attitudes of the kind we have been considering, there would be no science. In many instances, perhaps, when a branch of science has progressed to a certain point, men can afford to discard the scaffolding that was once important. Thus a good many scientists have discarded theology. But the faith that is required for scientific progress is not now less than it was in the early days, for new beliefs are replacing the old. We have already noted the relative novelty of the belief that science is an infinite quest, but other new beliefs, have also become increasingly accepted. There is the belief, for example, that the elegance of a theory is in some way connected with its truth; and the belief that explanations of nature must, in the last resort, be mathematical.

Intuitive Knowledge in Science and Mathematics

It is said in Cambridge circles that the late F. W. Aston could not have made his first mass spectrograph but for sheer intuition. For the positive rays to focus satisfactorily it was needful for many adjustments to be exactly right. The theory of how this might be done had not been adequately worked out at the time, yet, with almost uncanny skill, Aston was able to design and build an instrument that worked.

Modern developments also require as much *individual* faith as was ever the case. One well-known radio expert is renowned for getting the right answers to difficult problems. But he seems to do it by intuition. One of his scientific papers purported to establish an important and hitherto unknown result. The result was correct, yet his colleagues say that the paper contained forty mistakes—and by no means all trivial ones at that! The intuition was right, but the reasoning invented afterwards to justify it was wrong.

The element of faith required in the determination of structure by X-ray crystallography is considerable. It is impossible, logically, to work backwards from a pattern of dots to the arrangement of atoms within the "unit cell" which gave rise to the dots. First one must guess the 3-dimensional arrangement and then, by laborious mathematical methods which may take months or years to complete, one can find out unambiguously whether the guess was right. When great complexity is encountered the possible guesses run into millions. Therefore, for progress to be made at all, the guesses must, at least very frequently, be right. And again and again in the technical literature we find the significant expression "inspired guess" used. Indeed. no other words seem adequate. It is remarkable that in this field, both in Russia and in the West, those who have become eminent are often women, many women being, it seems, particularly gifted with intuitive powers.

Discoveries, quite obviously owing their origin to intuition, are particularly striking in the recent history of mathematics.[1] Ramanujan was educated in a primi-

[1] On this subject see the fascinating book of Jacques Hadamard, *op. cit.*

tive Indian school, and was later brought over to England where he worked with Hardy. He was gifted with amazing intuitive powers, and became the first coloured Fellow of Trinity College, Cambridge. It is said that he had little or no conception of the meaning of rigorous proof: "If a significant piece of reasoning occurred somewhere, and the total mixture of evidence and intuition gave him certainty, he looked no further," says Littlewood.[1]

Oliver Heaviside took delight in intuitional methods. His attitude was well summed up in his own words: "Am I to refuse to eat because I do not fully understand the mechanics of digestion?" To those who enthroned reason and insisted on sound proofs, "Heaviside's methods seemed a kind of blasphemy, a wilful sinning against the light," says Piagio.[2] Yet Heaviside did what other mathematicians could not do, and his remarkable method for solving differential equations, the best known of his discoveries, has been of untold value in many departments of science and technology.

Faith in Industry

Faith has operated not only in science and mathematics, but extensively, also, in industrial development. One of the most important strikes of oil in the post-war world was at West Edmond, Oklahoma, in 1943. Geological and geophysical prospecting, which included a few trial borings, indicated that the area was not

---

[1] Quoted, L. J. Mordell, *Nature*, 1941, **148**, 642.
[2] *Nature*, 1943, **152**, 93.

encouraging. But "definite faith on the part of the owner (Mr Gutowsky) that there was oil in the area"[1] followed by drilling to 7000 feet—with no trace of oil until almost this depth was reached—resulted in the discovery of an enormously rich oil-field.

Turning to another industry, it is said that Luther Burbank, the plant breeder, possessed an uncanny power of knowing which plants would be useful, but did not kimself know how he did it.[2]

Sometimes the faith is of a more general kind. Edison, perhaps the greatest inventor of modern times, held that "the existence of an intelligent Creator, a personal God, can, to my mind, almost be proved from chemistry". Repeated and seemingly endless failures in his experiments did not depress him, for he believed that God had the answer. Thus, whilst struggling with the problem of how to find a satisfactory material out of which to make electric light filaments, he could say: "Somewhere in God Almighty's workshop is a dense woody growth, with fibres almost geometrically parallel and with practically no pith, from which we can make the filament the world needs."[3]

Often faith takes the form of an inward certainty

[1] *Science News Letter*, 29th Dec. 1945. See also E. G. Dahlgren and D. O. Howard, *Mining and Metallurgy*, 1945, **26**, 607. This article states that Mr Gutowsky bought the land on the basis of statements by "doodlebugs" (American slang for unorthodox mineral diviners), but that no reputable company would take up exploration.

[2] *Luther Burbank: an Architect of Nature.* An autobiography (Thinkers' Library, No. 76), 1939. See esp. p. 40.

[3] The quotations are from G. P. Lathrop, "Talks with Edison", *Harper's Mag.* 1890, **19**, 425, and W. A. Simonds, *Edison: his Life, his Work, his Genius*, 1935.

that a particular method will solve some problem. A classical instance is that of Mond, who made use of nickel carbonyl—considered by all other chemists at the time to be an interesting laboratory curiosity unlikely to be of commercial importance—in order to recover nickel from its ores. There are probably few industries which do not owe their origins, in some degree at least, to faith of this kind.

Positive individual faith is invaluable for scientific and technological progress. Without it, science becomes a matter of playing around with no real aim in view. Without it, the difficulties that may be encountered are taken to mean that a job cannot be done. It is the positive faith that a thing *can* be done, whatever the difficulties, the faith that sees in the difficulties a challenge to further and yet further effort, which at last yields the finest fruits. The resemblance of such faith to the faith that is found in religion need hardly be stressed.

VI

SCIENCE
Its Christian Origins

THE conclusion we have drawn—that positive faith is a vital prerequisite of the progress of science—would seem to have an obvious consequence which we may now examine.

If faith is indeed necessary for science, then it might be supposed that Christianity and science would be intimately connected. For since Christianity is a religion of faith, it might be expected that, on the whole, Christians would find the exercise of faith easier than do those who are not Christians.

Origins of Science

Considering firstly, the origins of science, there is little doubt that the scientific movement of the seventeenth century owed its origin to the Christian faith. As a result of the Reformation the Bible had become available in the mother tongue of the people. Men began to read the book for themselves and many turned also to God's other book—the book of nature.

The belief that nature was to be regarded in this light supplied the motive for most, perhaps even all, of the work of the Royal Society in its early days. It is noteworthy that at least 90 per cent. of the foundation members of the Society were either Puritans or closely connected with Puritanism.[1]

The prevalent view at the beginning of the scientific movement was that, since God had created nature, only lazy and unthankful people would be uninterested in that upon which God had lavished so much thought and care. It was this belief, held with passion, which enabled the early investigators to overcome the discouragements and difficulties with which the beginnings of science were attended.

In those days the scientists, equipped with inferior instruments, poorly developed mathematics and impure chemicals—consisting for the most part of powdered minerals—found results painfully slow in coming. It was no easy matter to wrest nature's secrets. Nor were there convincing reasons for supposing that, when results had been obtained, mankind would be much the better for them. It was the passionate belief that it was an insult to the Creator to take no interest in His handiwork which gave men the courage to carry on.

Religion—An Objective of Science

Until relatively recently science remained faithful to its early theological beginnings. The widely held

[1] The literature on this subject is extensive. See particularly R. K. Merton, *Osiris*, 1938, **4**, pt. 2, and C. E. A. Turner, *Transactions of the Victoria Institute*, 1949, **81**, 85. There is also a useful chapter on the subject in A. F. Smethurst, *Modern Science and Christian Beliefs*, 1955, chapter 3.

belief that one of the chief purposes of science was to provide arguments for belief in God remained for two centuries. By the beginning of the nineteenth century it seemed that success in this direction was well within sight. At that time we find Sir David Brewster, President of the Royal Society, urging that science should be taught in the schools so that a new generation, no longer ignorant of the wonders of Creation, would find it all but impossible to become atheistic in their thinking or immoral in their ways. In the same period the famous Bridgewater treatises were published under the auspices of the Royal Society. Each was written by an eminent scientist in his own field and each was designed to show the wisdom and goodness of God in creation. We may cite two typical quotations of the period to illustrate the prevailing attitude. The object of science, according to Sir Humphrey Davy is "not only to apply the different substances in nature to the advantage, benefit and comfort of man, but likewise to set forth that wonderful and magnificent history of wisdom and intelligence which is written in legible characters both in the heavens and on earth".[1] And a popular encyclopaedia of 1843 states that, "In learning more and more of the wonderful works of the Creator we shall receive higher and yet higher motives to humble adoration of His (God's) infinite perfections."[2]

---

[1] Quoted by Sir E. K. Rideal, *Nature*, 1949, **163**, 431.
[2] *Popular Cyclopaedia*, 1843, p. 511.

Five Eminent Scientists

J. G. Crowther, in a well-known book, selects as the five most eminent British physical scientists of the nineteenth century, Davy, Faraday, Joule, Kelvin and Clerk-Maxwell.[1] All five were devout Christians.

Davy was, perhaps, the least religious of the five, but his beliefs are obvious from the passage quoted. Faraday was an ardent Christian, an elder of the Sandemanian sect and a regular Sunday preacher. He believed the Bible implicitly and his life of devotion to science was the direct outcome of his religious fervour.[2] Joule believed that, having learned to know and obey God, we must next seek to know His work—"The study of nature and her laws ... is essentially a holy undertaking." Kelvin's belief in Christianity is well known and his *Biography* shows that he took opportunities to talk with other scientific men on religious topics. Maxwell was fervently religious—he led in prayer extempore, knew the Bible almost by heart and was steeped in the old divines. That his science and his religion were intimately connected is obvious from his extempore prayers—for

[1] J. G. Crowther, *British Scientists of the Nineteenth Century*, 1935. It would not be unreasonable to include J. J. Thomson, who, at the end of the century, discovered the electron. J. J. Thomson, also, was a devout Christian who "kept his Bible on the library shelf nearest the door and read a few verses every night before retiring to rest" (J. A. Crowther, *Listener*, 16th Dec. 1948). It may be added that though Rutherford, his eminent pupil, was less devout he is nevertheless believed to have been a Christian. He often hummed hymns in the laboratory, and when a mutual friend was dying, he said to the Bishop of Derby, "You will pray for him, won't you?" (A. S. Eve, *Rutherford*, 1939.)

[2] The relation between Faraday's religion and his science is discussed by J. F. Riley, *The Hammer and the Anvil: a Background to Michael Faraday*, Clapham, Yorks, 1954.

example: "Teach us to study the works of Thy hands that we may subdue the earth to our use, and strengthen our reason for Thy service." The study of science was, for him, a way of serving God. "If we felt more distinctly our union to Christ." he wrote to his wife, "we would . . . work more willingly and intelligently along with the rest in promoting the health and growth of the body, by the use of every power which the spirit has distributed to us."[1]

These men, particularly the last four, were the men who, more than anyone else, *created* the scientific way of thinking. Yet they seem to have sensed no clash between this and their religion—rather the reverse. Physical science even today revolves round their discoveries: students still learn their conventions, derive their equations and use apparatus of their devising. Maxwell, in particular, saw far into the twentieth century. It would have struck all four as decidedly odd that students, a few generations hence, would think their stately edifice of science difficult to reconcile with faith in Christ.

Prayer and Scientific Work

No one who has the smallest insight into the mind of an ordinary Christian can seriously doubt that these men prayed about their scientific work. Faraday is often quoted (or misquoted) as saying that he kept his science and his religion in different compartments in

[1] L. Campbell and Wm. Garnett, *The Life of James Clerk-Maxwell*, 1882. Quotations from pp. 323, 328.

his mind.[1] Certainly he did not express his scientific results in religious language.[2] Yet we can be reasonably certain that again and again, when baffled by some problem, he prayed earnestly to God for the answer to be shown him.

Today it is sometimes said that science can have no direct connection with religion—for even Christians who are also scientists are atheists in their science. Remarks of this kind are unfair and untrue. Jesus told His disciples to keep their prayer life *secret*. And this is just what the men we have been speaking of did. We know little of their private lives. But that their science was, in some way, the flowering of their Christian faith can hardly be doubted.

There is so little literature on the private lives of scientists who are Christians that attention may be drawn at this point to a scientist of our own century concerning whom a good deal is known.

George Washington Carver (1864-1943) was an

[1] In his *Researches in Chemistry and Physics*, 1854, Faraday states that the scientific method will not confirm "the hope set before us" in the life to come. In this respect he sees an absolute distinction between religious and ordinary belief. But he goes on to quote St Paul's words with full approval: "The invisible things of Him since the creation of the world are clearly seen, being understood by the things that are made, even His eternal power and Godhead".

[2] He could use language in his laboratory notebook not far removed from religion, however. In starting his researches on the relation of electricity to gravity he writes: "It was almost with a feeling of awe that I went to work, for if the hope should prove well founded, how great and mighty and sublime in its hitherto unchangeable character is the force I am trying to deal with" (*Diary*, 25th Aug. 1849). His lectures on science could exert an almost religious effect. "To me his lecture was like Christ talking to the woman of Samaria," wrote John Tyndall (A. S. Eve and C. H. Creasey, *Life and Work of John Tyndall*, 1945, p. 50).

American negro of great brilliance. He believed that God had called him to save his people in the Southern States from disaster when the boll weevil was approaching their lands from the south. He knew that new crops must be found since the cotton was doomed. Peanuts seemed to be the answer. But how could they be sold? Carver claimed that he found the answer to this and hundreds of other problems by retreating to the woods in the early morning to be alone with God. He used to discuss all his work with God in prayer and he believed that God daily directed him concerning what to do next in the laboratory. He was able to find many hundreds of uses for peanuts—he invented peanut butter and introduced the oil to industry. He persuaded farmers to produce the new crop and in time saved his people, the negroes, from economic ruin. In other directions, also, his scientific life was extraordinarily fruitful.[1]

Though it is not often that men divulge the nature of their prayers, it is likely that Carver's practice is typical of most scientists who are practising Christians. If so, it is impossible to doubt that a large part of the fruitfulness of science has arisen simply through prayer and faith in God.

Influence of a Christian Culture

However we may interpret the fact, scientific development has only occurred in a Christian culture. The

[1] R. Holt, *pseud.*, *George Washington Carver*, 1947; A M. Pullen, *Despite the Colour Bar*, 1946; C. W. Wright, in *Journal of Chemical Education*, 1946, **23**, 268, gives an outline of Carver's scientific work.

ancients had brains as good as ours. In all civilizations —ancient Babylonia, Egypt, Greece, India, Rome, Persia, China, the Abassid empire and so on—science developed to a certain point and then stopped. It is easy to argue speculatively that, perhaps, science *might* have been able to develop in the absence of Christianity, but in fact it never did. And no wonder. For the non-Christian world believed that there was something ethically wrong about science. In Greece this conviction was enshrined in the legend of Prometheus, the fire-bearer and prototype scientist, who stole fire from heaven, thus incurring the wrath of the gods.

Historically it was Christianity and Christianity only which provided the firm bedrock of faith which made it possible for men to go exploring into the unknown, fearless of consequences. For the Christian knows, instinctively, that however world-shattering may be the conclusions he is forced to draw, they will never separate him from the love of God. If he is truly honest he cannot displease the Lord of Truth and has nothing to fear. In other cultures its religious and philosophical implications have soon made science appear foolish and dangerous and it has been destroyed. The same story repeated itself again and again in history.[1] Christianity proved to be the first and only religion capable of giving encouragement to advancing science.

[1] A. H. Compton, *The Freedom of Man*, 1935, pp. 17 ff. As an example H. Meyerhof in *The Legacy of Islam* (Eds. T. Arnold and A. Guillaume, 1931, p. 337) points out that early Islam tolerated science, but later persecution followed because science led "to loss of belief in the origin of the world and of the creation".

Having reached its present position, of course, it is possible for many scientists to discard the cradle that gave them birth. Over the past century science has become professional. It is encouraged in universities, is State-supported and pays handsome dividends to the industrialists. In this favoured climate it is no cause for surprise if many scientists can learn to exercise faith through the example of fellow-scientists alone. So we need hardly be surprised to find that not all scientists are Christians today—though the proportion who are so is certainly not less than that of professional people in general.[1] However, the overall picture is as we might have expected. The history of science, taken up to quite recent times, shows a very definite and intimate connection with Christianity. Those who have learned, in religion, to exercise faith have on the whole proved themselves better equipped to exercise faith in the field of science also.

Christianity—"Authoritarian" and "Free"

Before closing this discussion we must remind ourselves that—however much we may deplore the fact—Christianity is by no means a unity. If, then, we say that Christianity and science are connected, it becomes of interest to ask what kind of Christianity we have in mind.

Broadly speaking, we may distinguish two attitudes among nominal Christians—the *authoritarian* and the

[1] Malcolm Dixon, *Science and Irreligion* (Lecture given in Belfast, 1952. Published by R. S. C. F., 39 Bedford Sq., London, W.C.1.)

free. The first attitude is encouraged by those sects that have a hierarchy in charge or who, through concern for orthodoxy, show more interest in maintaining their doctrinal position intact than in discovering new truth. At the other extreme are those sects which insist that a large measure of latitude of thought is essential in the Christian church and believe that it is wrong to persecute and expel Christians because, often in a purely temporary phase of their lives, they express doubt concerning a Christian doctrine.[1] In the last resort it is a tenet of such sects that Christian love, understanding and forbearance are more important than intellectual doctrinal soundness.

As we might well expect, the relationship between science and Christianity is far more intimate with free Christianity than with Christianity of the authoritarian type. The difference is quite startling—a fact to which attention has been drawn by almost every historian who has studied the point.

In illustration we may cite two facts out of scores. In the two centuries covering the period 1666-1883 the Academy of Paris elected 80 Protestant scientists but only 18 Roman Catholics as foreign members. Since France was predominantly Catholic and Protestants were a minority in Europe the figures are all the more

[1] In New Testament times Christians who behaved immorally in such a way as to bring discredit on the Church, were excommunicated. But excommunication for wrong ideas seems not to have been practised. "Antichrists" in the Church often left of their own accord, but were not cast out (1 John 2.19). St Paul makes no proposal that the Judaisers who undermined the faith of the Church should be excommunicated (Gal. 5.12).

striking. The same disparity is shown by elections to other learned societies.[1]

Secondly, several investigations into the religious background of American scientists have been conducted in recent years. The productivity of scientists as between one Christian tradition and another has been found to vary enormously—some sects are several hundred times as productive as others. Sects which have a strong Protestant and usually Puritan background, combined with freedom and tolerance of the individual prove to be the most productive.[2]

[1] R. K. Merton, *Sociological Review*, 1936, **28**, 1. See also *Osiris*, 1938, vol. 4, pt. 2, and Max Weber, *The Protestant Ethic and the Spirit of Capitalism*, Eng. Trans., 1930.
[2] H. C. Lehman and P. A. Willy, *Scientific Monthly*, Dec. 1931 **33**, 544, R. H. Knapp and H. B. Goodrich, *Origins of American Scientists*, Univ. of Chicago Press, 1952.

VII

THE CERTAINTY OF SCIENCE

In past chapters we have frequently had cause to comment on the striking resemblances that exist between scientific and religious faith. But there are also some apparent differences which may seem to make an analogy between the two spheres remote and far-fetched.

Certainty in Science and Uncertainty in Religion

Most people, at one time or another, have been struck by the contrast between the certainty of science and what seems like the uncertainty of religion. We do not find scientists today debating whether the formula of water is H_2O or HO; or divided concerning whether or not the blood is pumped round the body by the heart. There is no controversy as to whether the earth is round or flat, or whether the moon is held in its orbit by gravity or by an angel which pushes it along its path. The scientific method has led to definite results which are accepted by everyone as true. But in religion it is otherwise. There is no proof of God's existence which commands general assent. Not everyone is convinced that Jesus rose from the dead. And even amongst Christians we find no agreement as to precisely what Jesus taught on many subjects, such as the kind of Church He intended to leave behind on earth.

We may freely admit that the contrast between science and religion is here most marked. But before jumping to conclusions, let us examine the "certainty of science" a little more closely.

In doing so we at once note a curious fact. The "certainty of science" is found only in matters which do not affect us personally. It is found in science, as in religion, that when strong prejudices are aroused, even straightforward evidence fails to carry conviction—or even to be accepted as evidence at all.

Past Scientific Prejudices

In the nineteenth century most people entertained strong opinions as to what they expected nature to be like. Most of the basic units of nature were supposed to be infinitely divisible. This view, which was simply taken for granted, had the advantage of making calculations easy. The infinitesimal calculus made it possible to carry out calculations on the speeding up of rotating wheels, the emptying of tanks of water, the charging of condensers with electricity and so forth. In all cases you had but to use the calculus in order to sum up an infinite series of infinitely small changes and you knew the answer.

The opposite assumption, that energy, light, matter, electricity and magnetism consisted of small units which could not be subdivided, hardly received serious attention. No one imagined that it would only be possible to speed up a railway engine by adding energy to its rotating wheels in a series of jerks!

In chemistry the notion of indivisable atoms began to get a look in again (it had been accepted in the seventeenth century and abandoned in the eighteenth) after 1800—but in other fields natural philosophers did not take the notion too seriously until the end of the nineteenth century. Wilhelm Ostwald, in his Faraday Lecture to the Chemical Society, still used highly ingenious arguments against the existence of atoms as late as 1904.

All the same, atoms were orthodox from about 1800. But the scientists of the day were extraordinarily slow in taking the next step. Faraday showed that a certain amount of electricity, or exactly twice or three times this quantity, was always associated with an atom in a conducting solution. The obvious implication was that electricity, like matter, consisted of particles. This was mentioned as a possibility, but the matter was not pursued. Right up to the present century the scientific world was blind to the existence of the electron or "atom" of electricity. Today, even the schoolboy is amazed at this blindness, since the nineteenth-century scientists had all the important facts before them. They knew that matter consisted of atoms, and they knew that in solution an equal number of charged atoms of whatever kind always carried an equal quantity of electricity or a simple multiple of this quantity. The conclusion that electricity, like chemical atoms, is atomic seems to follow logically. Yet in the nineteenth century prevailing ideas about the way the universe was made prevented recognition of the obvious.

Again, indications that atoms of heavier elements were built up from hydrogen or from some other lighter element were not lacking even at the beginning of the nineteenth century. The evidence became much stronger towards the end of the century when Mendeleef arranged the elements in accordance with a natural classification. But though the possibility was mooted from time to time, it met with strong opposition and even Mendeleef frowned upon it. Again prejudice was the cause—we shall later have reason to examine the nature of the prejudice in this instance.

Failures in Imagination

Another kind of prejudice is due to a failure to envisage the future. Thus former generations of men had become so accustomed to seeing objects in their "natural" size that, for many years, the obvious scientific possibilities inherent in lenses were simply overlooked. It appears that simple lenses were known in ancient times but the telescope and compound microscope are modern discoveries.

Again, Clerk-Maxwell showed that Faraday's ideas led naturally to the concept of electro-magnetic radiation and Hertz verified his prediction by detecting wireless waves. The possibility of sending messages by wireless should have been obvious at once, but it was a long time before the coming of wireless telegraphy. The story is told that in 1879 D. F. Hughes, inventor of the printing telegraph, made a simple coherer with graphite carbons. He joined this to a cell and a telephone. With this arrangement he heard sounds in the telephone whenever an induction coil, giving sparks, was in operation some distance away. He demonstrated the experiment to a number of people, including the then President of the Royal Society, but received no encouragement. He was assured that there was nothing new in his work: it merely illustrated the principle of electromagnetic induction which had been discovered long ago by Faraday. Discouraged, he dropped the work—otherwise radiotelegraphy would have developed fifteen years earlier than it did.[1]

Even when, in due course, many important discoveries and inventions at last made their appearance most people were at first profoundly sceptical. Edison showed how the human voice could be recorded and played back at will, but many people, when they saw a demonstration of the apparatus, supposed that a ventriloquist was hidden behind the scenes who was mimicking peoples' voices and making them seem to come from Edison's mysterious box. One man remained unconvinced until he had gabbled a long passage in Greek to the phonograph and had heard the same sounds repeated back at the same high speed. This, he thought, was more than could be expected of a conjuror.

When Daguerre attempted to sell shares in the first company to exploit his newly discovered way of fixing images, the Parisian public were so reluctant to believe

[1] Sir Ambrose Fleming, *Proc. Physical Soc.*, 1939, **51**, 383, (p. 390).

in the possibility of photography that they would not risk their money.[1] When the telephone was first invented, a technical official of the British Post Office declared that it was a toy of no practical use.[2] When the first news reached England that Röntgen's X-rays would pass through matter the "journalistic nonsense" was greeted with ridicule.[3]

Again, in the early days of railways, high speeds were considered dangerous, impossible, or both—despite the fact that birds fly much faster than any vehicle then thought possible. In the *Creevey Papers*, one of a party who travelled at 23 m.p.h. thus recorded his impressions of the journey: "frightful—impossible to divest yourself of the notion of instant death—it gave me a headache which has not yet left me—some damnable thing must come of it . . ." At the British Association in 1836 someone ventured to prophecy that speeds of 50 m.p.h. would one day become possible!

In 1862 the *Lancet* appointed a commision to report on the "Influence of Railway Travelling on Health". When the report was published the learned doctors told of the desiccating effect on the skin caused by high speeds, of the "reiterated concussions" on the spinal centres, of "Incessant vibrations on the tympanum", of the "rapid ageing of Season-Ticket holders" and of the terrible psychological strain of the ever-present fear of death as proved by the fact that "when a whistle sounds its shrill alarm, a head is projected from every

[1] W. J. Harrison. *History of Photography*, 1888, p. 22.
[2] Sir Ambrose Fleming, *Memories of a Scientific Life*, 1935, p. 79.
[3] H. Dale [Sir], *loc. cit.*

window".[1] When trains arrived for the first time in out-of-the-way villages, people peeped under the engines looking for the horses inside or betted as to their number.[2] Coming to our own century, we are reminded of how, in 1906, the engineering correspondent of *The Times* stated that "all attempts at artificial aviation . . . are not only dangerous to human life but foredoomed to failure from an engineering point of view".

This blindness to the possibilities inherent in science is of particular interest since it is of the same kind as the blindness, or lack of faith, to which our Lord so often referred. In the history of technology the faith of the grain of mustard seed has too often been lacking— lacking amongst the scientists and technicians as well as among the common people. Only after two world wars have men awoken to the possibilities for good or evil inherent in a proper control of the forces of nature.

Modern Blindness

Looking back, it is easy to see the mistakes of others. But it is likely, of course, that we too allow prejudice to blind us to the obvious implications of science in our own day. A future generation may be astounded at the way in which, knowing full well the dangers involved

[1] *The Lancet Report on the Influence of Railway Travelling on Public Health*, price 1s. from Mr Hardwicke of Piccadilly. The *Report* is published in full in the *Lancet*, 1862, vol. i, from Jan. to Mar.

[2] An amusing story is told of a vicar who brought his entire village to the station when the first train came and carefully explained to them how the engine worked. They were deeply interested and nodded assent approvingly. But when he had finished, one of them said; "Yes, yes, we understand all that, but it really *has* horses inside, hasn't it?"

for humanity at large, nations have gone on developing missiles and nuclear explosives for their own national advantages, irrespective of the welfare of mankind at large. As E. M. Butler well points out, the alchemists of a former age often ruined their lives in their search for the Philosophers' Stone, but their work "is on a much higher level than the invention of poison gases and gigantic instruments of destruction".[1]

Again, those who live in days to come may be equally surprised at the way in which, with all our knowledge of genetics, we have done so little to improve the human race. In this connection J. B. S. Haldane and others have drawn attention to the possibilities of identifying human genes by means of taste and smell reactions—but although institutes for the study of such matters were founded in Germany and Russia before World War II, both were closed for political reasons— the Germans objecting that the early results were beginning to throw doubt upon the supremacy of the Aryan race and the Russians because the results led to scepticism of the doctrine that all men are equal.

Further Examples are not Lacking

Though the dangers of tobacco smoking have been discovered and confirmed in every industrialized country in the world, vested interest prevents its abolition—and this despite the fact that one per cent. of the incriminating evidence cited against a newly introduced drug would at once cause it to be scheduled as a poison.

[1] E. M. Butler, *The Myth of the Magus*, C.U.P. 1948, p. 161.

Nevertheless there are many able minds who twist the evidence to prove the opposite conclusion or side-track the issue to distract attention from a very clear "finding of science". Fluoridation of water supplies and psychical research furnish further rather similar examples.

There is, thus, no reasonable doubt that the "certainty of science" disappears at once when philosophical prejudice, politics, personal habits and similar factors enter the picture. Even the clearest evidence then becomes blurred and it is always possible to quote eminent authorities on both sides of a controversy.

On such occasions the usual retort is to assert that certainty is just round the corner, that science will achieve it shortly but that more research must first be carried out. In the end there will be doubt no longer.

To say this, however, is to evade the issue. That smoking often produces cancer was known at least thirty years ago. Though great improvements have taken place in the techniques of psychical research, nothing really new has been added to our knowledge of the subject for at least a century. But on both issues controversy and doubt continue. And in every such case a small fraction of the evidence would be accepted as conclusive if emotional factors were *not* involved.

Humility and Private Judgment

To return to our subject, many people think it odd that, if Christianity is true, it does not command general assent—at least from highly trained intellects. How can the evidence that is sometimes given for the belief that

God created the world, or that Jesus rose from the dead, be considered convincing when it is easy to quote well-known philosophers at universities who say they are not convinced? If religion rests on argument, then who are we to say that we are more logical than they?

In view of a similar state of affairs in the scientific world, this fact really calls for neither surprise nor comment. Suffice it to say that the dangerous head of authoritarianism is here raising its head. Does the schoolboy who can see the fallacies in nineteenth-century scientific thought think he has a better brain than a Faraday or a Clerk-Maxwell? Let us hope not. It is possible to be intellectually humble and yet to sense the amazing prejudice, blindness and intellectual blunders of those who, on ninety-nine occasions out of a hundred, may be trusted to use their minds more logically than we.[1]

If an argument is convincing we must accept it: it is no cause for alarm if half the world declares that it is unconvincing—nor even, indeed, if I am the only person in the world to see its force. And if it is perfectly plain that prejudice enters the picture, we do not need religion to remind us that even the wisest of men can argue stupidly.

[1] Bertrand Russell's *Why I am not a Christian*, 1927, affords a good example of this. The prejudice exhibited could not be bettered. A kind and understanding analysis of Russell's arguments was met by a sheepish reply in which Russell admitted that his opponent had been fairer than he (*The Philosophy of Bertrand Russell* (Ed. P. A. Schilpp), Library of Living Philosophers, 5, Evanston, Ill., 1944). Yet Russell republished the offending essay unaltered in 1957 (*Why I am not a Christian and other Essays*). See also, H. G. Wood, *Why Mr Bertrand Russell is not a Christian*, 1928.

84

VIII

"THINGS THAT ARE NOT"

In the modern age when a successful scientific career depends increasingly upon specialization, academic attainment and prestige, any possible connection between scientific and religious belief is apt to seem far-fetched and remote. What has the complex scientific belief, formed in the minds of highly trained specialists who could discover nothing without years of preliminary study, to do with that simple Christian faith which has always found acceptance among the unlearned and ignorant? Have we not here a case of knowledge set against ignorance?

Young Discoverers

Once again, however, a more careful study of the facts shows that, even in this respect, science and religion are not dissimilar. Scientific discovery has often by-passed the specialists. Many great discoveries were made by young men whose vision proved clearer and more far-sighted than that of their superiors, possessed of more knowledge and experience than they.[1]

[1] On this subject see particularly, Robert H. Murray, *Science and Scientists in the Nineteenth Century* (Sheldon Press), 1925.

Lyell's main ideas in geology came to him when he was 20 and Pasteur separated racemic acid into the *dextro* and *laevo* forms of tartaric acid at the same age. Perkin made the first aniline dye in a shed in the back garden at the age of 18. Einstein was 18 when he first conceived the theory of relativity. Arrhenius put forward the theory of electrolytic dissociation at the age of 24 and Bohr conceived his theory of atomic structure at the age of 28, Crookes discovered thallium by means of the spectroscope when he was 29. Moseley discovered the K spectrum of the elements at the age of 26. Gilchrist solved the outstanding technological problem of his day—to make steel from iron ore containing phosphorus—when he was 28. Van't Hoff was aged 22 and Le Bel 27 in 1874 when they put forward their theory of optical and geometrical isomerism and so laid the foundation of all subsequent progress in stereo-chemistry from that day to this. B. K. Sing points out that, until very recent times at least, every main advance in this field was made by men below the age of 30.[1]

The germs of many successful inventions, too, have begun to mature in youthful minds. Thus Edwin Land conceived "polaroid" at the age of 20 when he had just entered Harvard University, and he worked alone on the project until 1928.[2]

It is the same in biological research. Here also the main fundamental advances have been made by

[1] B. K. Sing, *Jour. Indian Chemical Soc.*, 1932, 9, 18.
[2] J. Jewkes, D. Sawers and R. Stillerman, *The Sources of Invention*, 1958, p. 382.

well-known American college, while two were self-taught.[1]

Discoverers Ridiculed, Persecuted or Ignored

The fact that discoveries have come from those considered least competent to make them often involved discoverers in ridicule and even persecution from those who thought they were better and wiser.

Vesalius, founder of modern anatomy, was so disgusted by the opposition to his book *Fabrica Humani Corporis* that he finally relinquished research altogether. Ohm was regarded as a fanatic. Thomas Young was the object of merciless ridicule. Trevithick was criticized for introducing high-pressure steam in boilers. Watt said that the boilers would explode, causing loss of life and that the fanatic who invented them deserved death by hanging.[2] Morton in America (who first used nitrous oxide to extract a tooth) was ruthlessly persecuted and finally, in misery and poverty, took his life.[3] The story of Semmelweis, who discovered that in hospitals doctors and students were infecting patients with puerperal fever, is also one of unrelieved tragedy.[4] The biographies of Lister (who introduced antiseptic surgery) and Simpson (who introduced chloroform as an anaesthetic) abound with the stories of the ignorant opposition with which they had to contend. The famous

[1] C. A. Kraus, *Science*, 1939, **89**, 276.
[2] J. Jewkes *et al.*, *op. cit.*, p. 40.
[3] Rene Fülöp-Miller, *Triumph over Pain*, 1938.
[4] W. J. Sinclair, *Semmelweis, His Life and Doctrine*, 1909.

young men.[1] The most creative years are from 30 to 40 (reckoned on a basis of quantity published), but originality seems often to decline in the twenties.

Invading the Fields of Others

So difficult is it for those who are highly trained in their own field of knowledge to adopt a child-like approach that we find, as we might expect, that great discoveries have often been made by those who have invaded a field of knowledge other than their own.[2] Davy, who had never been down a coal-mine invented the miner's lamp, for which he was later famed, within a fortnight or so of starting work on the problem. Pasteur, on being invited to investigate the disease of the silkworm which was crippling French industry, replied: "Remember, if you please, that I have never even touched a silkworm." At the time he did not even know that there was a chrysalis inside the silkworm cocoon. Yet within six years he had accomplished what had proved beyond the experts in the industry.

Arrhenius remarked concerning those who developed the law of the indestructability of energy: "It is very significant that not one of these men was a scientist by profession."[3] "It is no accident", wrote Darlington, "that bacteria were first seen under the microscope by a draper, that stratigraphy was first understood by a

[1] Beveridge, *op. cit.*, p. 157, gives a similar list of biological discoveries in which only the discovery of insulin (Banting, aged 31) was made by a man over 30.
[2] H. C. Lehman, *Science*, 1943, **98**, 393.
[3] S. Arrhenius, *Life of the Universe*, 1909, vol. II, p. 228.

canal engineer, that oxygen was first isolated by a Unitarian minister, that the discovery of infection was first established by a chemist, the theory of heredity by a monastic school-teacher, and the theory of evolution by a man who was unfitted to be a university instructor in either botany or zoology".[1] In the mathematical field, we are reminded that "analytic geometry was the independent invention of two men [Fermat, a lawyer, and Descartes, a philosopher], neither of whom was a professional mathematician".[2]

Speaking of engineering inventions, Dickinson reminds us, too, that Arkwright, who invented spinning, was a barber and that Huntsman, who invented crucible steel, was a clockmaker. He concludes that it is "no disadvantage to an inventor to be outside the industry in which his invention is to find scope, as he has no preconceived notions to overcome".[3] The story has recently been brought up to date in a careful investigation of inventions of the present century.[4] Gillette, we are reminded, was a travelling salesman in crown corks, Dunlop was a veterinary surgeon, Midgley (inventor of lead tetraethyl as an antiknock in petrol and of Freon as a refrigerant—two of the greatest chemical inventions of this century) was a mechanical engineer.

We who live on this earth can gaze out into space and can see the shapes of other galaxies easily enough; but it is difficult to make out that of our own. In like

[1] C. D. Darlington, *The Conflict of Science and Society*, 1948, p. 5.
[2] Carl Boyer, *History of Analytic Geometry*, N.Y. 1956, p. 74.
[3] H. W. Dickinson, *Proc. Instit. Mechanical Engineers*, 1934, **126**, 3.
[4] J. Jewkes *et al.*, *op. cit.*, p. 118.

manner, becoming immersed in the technica subject may blind us to facts which ought to b and which an outsider can see easily enough.

Provided, then, we are thinking of fun scientific truths and not their mere refinem applications, it is true to say that one does no be a scientist to discover truth in science.

Ignorant and Unqualified

Again, it has frequently happened that d and inventions have been made by those who generation, were considered ignorant and foo In many instances discoverers did not receive that education could offer in their day. And other instances they were subjected to ridi every obstacle was put in their way.

Contemporaries of Brand, the seventeentl discoverer of phosphorus, belittled him as an ig who did not even know Latin.[1] Similar critici levelled at many of the earlier discoverers common too, in the early days of the Royal Sc people to poke fun at those learned men wh their time upon objects so small that it needed scope to see them, or worried their heads ab intangible substances as air.

Of the five greatest physical scientists n America from colonial days up to 1880 (1 Rumford, Joseph Henry, Henry A. Rowla Willard Gibbs), only one was the produ

[1] J. R. Partington, *Science Progress*, 1936, **30**, 40

chemist Kolbe attacked Van't Hoff and Le Bel viciously for their theory of isomerism, speaking of the "fanciful nonsense" and "supernatural explanations" of these "unknown chemists". Joule had papers rejected by the Royal Society, as did also Fourier by the French Academy and Jenner by another learned society. Avogadro's famous law, fundamental to chemistry and physics, though put forward in 1808, was neglected for fifty years. Frankland's paper at the Royal Society, identifying lightning with electricity, was received with patronizing sarcasm. Newlands, who came near to discovering the periodic law of chemistry, was asked facetiously at the Chemical Society whether he had ever tried arranging the elements alphabetically and, if so, whether chemical resemblances again emerged. Lobachevsky, in his lifetime, was ridiculed for his discovery of non-Euclidian geometry; his ideas were only accepted twelve years after his death.[1]

In our own century Gillette was told by the steel experts that his idea for a safety razor was impossible, while his friends thought his invention was a joke. When in 1921, Sir Alexander Fleming gave his first paper on the antibiotic *lysozyme*, the reception it received was "cold beyond belief".[2] Whittle, inventor of the jet engine, complains of the endless difficulties that were placed in his path, and of the treatment still meted out to inventors.[3] C. F. Carlson, inventor of xerography (a form of photography which makes use of electro-

[1] *Nature*, 1957, **179**, 1176.
[2] *Life, op. cit.*
[3] Whittle, Frank [Sir], *Jet, The Story of a Pioneer*, 1953 p. 203.

static charges), says that most of his friends looked upon him with scorn for wasting his time.

Today, the world looks to the atom to provide man with energy in years to come. It is easy to forget what took place within the lifetime of older people. Rutherford was sarcastically asked why he insisted on believing that the atoms had "an incurable suicidal mania". The eminent chemist H. E. Armstrong professed himself "astonished at the feats of imagination" of this young man. At McGill University, where Rutherford obtained a post, his colleagues let it be known that they feared lest his radical views on the transformation of matter would bring discredit on the University.[1] When Otto Hahn discovered radiothorium in 1904, Boltwood, of Yale University, wrote to Rutherford to tell him that Hahn's radiothorium was "a compound of thorium and stupidity."[2]

How easily we might add concerning all these men, and many others besides, the epitaph of Hebrews (11.38)—"Of whom the world was not worthy."

The scientist who develops his ideas along the tracks laid by others before him is safe enough, for he treads on no man's corns. But it is true to say that whenever fundamentally new ideas, out of harmony with the science of the age, have been proposed, those who have suggested them have usually been subjected to persecution, ridicule or both. As Murray puts it:

Is there any punishment equal to that which, in

[1] A. S. Eve, *Rutherford*, 1939.
[2] *New Scientist*, 20th June 1957.

the name of science and with the full authority of science, has been inflicted upon Jenner and Simpson, Lyell and Helmholtz, Joule and Darwin, Pasteur and Lister, in some cases by ignoring their epoch-making ideas, and in others by fighting them to the death? Did any set of men so torture the body as scientists tortured the minds of these discoverers by bitterly criticizing them? One would have thought that the thanks of the whole scientific world would at once have been their rightful due. In not a single case was this so.[1]

Reasons for Opposition

Reasons for this persecution and ridicule are not far to seek. Jealousy is easily aroused in science, just as it was in early Christian days when the preaching of the Gospel to the Gentiles provoked the Jews to jealousy, or when, as happened repeatedly throughout the ages, spiritual awakening came to simple Christians, to the chagrin of the orthodox hierarchy.

It is legitimate to point out also that those who suffered for their ideas had often themselves to blame—as, for example, Paracelsus, Charles Babbage and Semmelweis, all of whom were as conspicuously lacking in tact, as were many of the religious reformers of by-gone days—the early Quakers, for instance. Many discoverers and inventors, too, have failed to acquire the knowledge and self-discipline that are necessary if ideas are to be presented intelligibly to others. It is perilously easy to employ an ill-considered jargon, filled

[1] R. H. Murray, *op. cit.* p. 316.

with clichés and inaccuracies, and there is little to choose between ugly scientific jargon and the jargon of theology. Yet these are not the only important factors. One of the basic reasons for opposition to new ideas in science is the simple one that radically new ideas look foolish.

The Foolishness of Novelty

This is a point about which all writers appear to be agreed. "If you have had your attention directed to the novelties in thought in your own lifetime, you will have observed that almost all really new ideas have a certain aspect of foolishness when they are first produced," writes Whitehead.[1] Frenkel, speaking of the radically new ideas in physics, remarks: "A characteristic feature of any new theory, which does not try to fit new facts to an already established representation . . . is its irrationality from the point of view of previous ideas."[2] And another writer, also speaking of scientific innovations, remarks that often "they were quite illogical and foolish in the opinion of men of wider experience", but that nevertheless "less daring, more experienced and in fact more logical individuals" would in most cases never have succeeded.[3]

In the field of mathematics there are, perhaps, an unusual number of examples of mere foolishness winning the day. Who, for example, could have been

[1] A. N. Whitehead, *Science and the Modern World*, (1926), 1932 ed. p. 60.
[2] J. Frenkel, *Nature*, 1944, **154**, 417.
[3] J. J. Abel, *Journal of Chemical Education*, 1930, **7**, 283.

more stupid than Girolamo Cardan (1501-76), who knew full well that no negative number has a square root. Yet, as Hadagard puts it, he "deliberately commits that absurdity and begins to calculate on such imaginary quantities. One would describe this as pure foolishness . . ."[1] Without that foolishness much of the huge subsequent progress in mathematics would have been impossible and the debt of technology to Cardan can scarcely be exaggerated.

Subsequent developments in mathematics illustrate the same point. Riemann constructed a geometry based upon the notion that more than one parallel straight line can pass through a point—though the opposite axiom has seemed self-evident to mankind since the days of Euclid. Branches of algebra in which xy is not equal to yx have been developed, and so on. These and other developments which all seem so contrary to common sense have proved of great value in the progress of man's understanding of nature.

Turning to physical theories, it is well known that Planck's suggestion that energy behaved like particles seemed absurd in his day. Hyman Levy reminds us of how, in 1912, when he was listening to Einstein lecturing on Relativity, "a number of German professors stamped out, enraged at such unimaginable nonsense."[2] Again, when in 1934 Ida Noddack suggested that uranium atoms underwent fission, both Fermi and Hahn regarded the idea as absurd.[3]

---

[1] J. Hadagard, *op. cit.*, p. 122.
[2] *New Scientist*, 27th Feb. 1958, p. 32.
[3] S. J. Redstone, *New Scientist*, 4th Sept. 1958.

In the history of science we often find that common people have had much sounder scientific ideas than the wise and prudent of their day. It was the plumbers who told Galileo that it was impossible to suck water up more than a certain distance by means of a pump, a view quite contrary to what the learned world supposed. The sophisticated Greeks of ancient times rejected the germ theory of disease, mainly, it has been said, because the barbarians held it. On many occasions scientists have learned of cures for diseases from simple folk with their herbal remedies, hoary with age. We are reminded in all this of our Lord's words: "I thank thee, Father, that thou hast hid these things from the wise and prudent and revealed them unto babes."

Religious Parallels

These considerations show once again that the link between scientific and religious faith, far from being nebulous, is very intimate indeed. At every point Christianity offers close parallels.

Religious truth, like scientific truth, may by-pass the scholars of the day. It was ignorant fishermen who founded the Christian Church which became far more influential than the religion of the scholarly rabbis, whilst the religions of Greece and Rome declined and were no more. The founders of the Church were young men too, and the only trained theological scholar amongst them, St Paul, was also young. The doctrine they taught seemed mere foolishness to the world in general—"the foolishness of preaching", St Paul calls it. It fitted in with none of the expectations of the day. The Jews sought after a sign and the Greeks after wisdom, but the new religion pleased neither. The enthusiasm with which it was preached seemed like the results of intoxication—"these men are full of new wine". And it seemed to contemporaries, as to Celsus in Rome in the following century,[1] that the learning of the Christians was that of the common people rather than the learning of the scholar.

The word of the cross is to them that are perishing foolishness; but unto us which are saved it is the power of God. For it is written, I will destroy the wisdom of the wise and the prudence of the prudent will I reject. Where is the wise? Where is the scribe? Where is the disputer of this world? Hath not God made foolish the wisdom of the world . . . God chose the foolish things of the world, that he might put to shame them that are wise; and God chose the weak things of the world, that he might put to shame the things that are strong; and the base things of the world, and the things that are despised did God choose, yea, and the things that are not, that he might bring to nought the things that are.

(I Cor. 1.18-28).

But why, we ask, did God so make the world that truth could not be discovered by worldly wisdom? St Paul's answer is convincing: "That no flesh should

---

[1] R. Walzer, *Galen on Jews and Christians*, 1949.

glory in the presence of God." If mere cleverness could unlock nature's secrets and divine truth, discoverers would become insufferably conceited. They might rightly point to a world transformed by their own efforts and so force themselves to the top of society, doing untold harm to themselves and to all men. If discovery depends upon knowledge and upon experience primarily, rather than upon openness of mind and ability to catch hold of ideas which seem to be given us from without, then younger men would discover little or nothing. Zest and interest, both in religion and in science, would be undermined. Instead, God has linked faith and humbleness of mind with discovery—the greatest men in science and those with the clearest insights into theology are often the most humble of men.

Just as university professors of science have, in the past, often shown themslves incapable of appraising radically new scientific ideas, so ecclesiastical authorities and professors of theology are in no position to judge new discoveries of religious truth. And this, no doubt, is why Jesus insisted that men have a Father in heaven who is their only Teacher and so are forbidden to call any man on earth Rabbi, Teacher, Father.

The Bible repeatedly draws attention to the fact that both great leaders and religious truths, like their scientific counterparts, come from unexpected quarters. From the days of the Judges onwards we have illustrations of the rule that "base things . . . hath God chosen to confound the wise". Jeptha was thrown out by his brethren, Gideon was the least important member of his family and Saul came from the most insignificant family of the smallest tribe of Israel. Jacob, David and Solomon were younger sons of their fathers, and prophets such as Amos arose from the common people. Often the message came through despised foreigners: "By men of strange lips and of another tongue will he speak to this people" (Isa. 28.11). The claims of Jesus, born in a manger because there was no room in the inn at Bethlehem, are easily dismissed: "Can any good thing come out of Nazareth?"[1]; the disciples are unlearned fishermen; Paul becomes the greatest apostle of all, though he had not known our Lord in the flesh and received no apostolic authority from Peter or James at Jerusalem.[2] The Biblical story is always the same.[3] The stone which the builders reject becomes the head of the corner. Leadership and truth come from unexpected sources. The first shall be last and the last first.

Ancient Jews were enraged when attention was drawn to facts such as these. Both Christians and scientists in later times have only too often been equally bigoted. And, needless to say, St Paul's teaching on

---

[1] John, 1.46. Compare also John 7.27; "We know this man whence he is: but when the Christ cometh, no one knoweth whence he is."

[2] Galatians, chaps. 1 and 2.

[3] To the author, at least, this fact makes it extremely difficult to understand the attitude of those who advocate authoritarian forms of Christianity. Catholic apologists often argue that a specialized hierarchy is necessary in religion just as it is in, say, medicine or science, and that the individual should subordinate his opinions to the experts. To offer such advice in medicine, science or theology is the best possible way to hinder all discovery.

the subject sends the modern atheist into hysterics.[1]
But in the end, though the mills of God grind slowly,
the foolishness of God confounds the wisdom of the wise.

[1] Thus Nietzche speaks of ". . . 'the wisdom of the world' which an
impudent windbag tries in vain to confound by 'the foolishness of
preaching' " (*The Antichrist*, Eng. ed., p. 193). Similarly Llewelyn
Powys disdainfully asks; "And who was it but he Paul . . . who found
out, through his deep taboos and totems, half Jewish, half God
knows what, the world-undermining doctrine about the weak overcoming the strong, the foolish overcoming the clever and . . . things
that are not overcoming things that are?" (*The Pathetic Fallacy*, 1930.
p. 42).

IX

AN ANALOGY

The Story of Stas

Soon after John Dalton, the Quaker, had propounded the atomic theory in the early years of the nineteenth century, Prout advanced the view that the various atoms were built up out of a single building block—hydrogen. In support of this he pointed out that many of the weights of the atoms, as then known, appeared to be simple multiples of the weight of the hydrogen atom.[1]

At this time Stas was a young man. On hearing of Prout's views he was fascinated. In later years he recounted his experiences more or less in the following words: "In my youth I was an ardent believer in the unity of matter as expounded by Prout. I was so well convinced about his theory that I became eager to furnish additional proofs by redetermining more accurately the atomic weights of those elements where the atomic weight numbers were not an even multiple of hydrogen. I simply imagined that more careful

---

[1] The weights of the atoms were not known unambiguously at the time, thus carbon and oxygen, respectively, appeared to be either 6 or 12 and 8 or 16 times as heavy as the hydrogen atom but this uncertainty did not affect the argument.

determinations would have eliminated these irregularities. But the more I worked, the more I perfected my methods, the more I eliminated any errors of experimentation, so much the more did my results contradict my dearest hopes. Finally I had to admit that I was beaten and had spent the most important part of my life in killing my first love as a theory."[1]

As a result of this work, Stas became a powerful opponent of Prout's theory. It was largely due to him that chemists throughout the world ceased to take that theory seriously any longer. So certain was he of his newly acquired views that he could write: "I have arrived at the absolute conviction, the absolute certainty, so far as it is possible for a human being to attain to certainty in such matters, that the law of Prout is nothing but an illusion, a mere speculation contradicted by experiment."[2]

Yet every schoolboy knows today that Stas was wrong and Prout was right.

Confusion of Faith with Hypothesis

In this story we have an example of a strong positive faith in a man of science. It was a faith on which he acted, dedicating his life to the determination of atomic weights. But he confused faith with hypothesis. He imagined that the faith with which he started was of

[1] This story was told by Stas to Baekeland, when the latter was a young man. It is related by James Kendall, *Chemistry and Industry Review*, 1949, p. 67 (Jan. 29).
[2] Quoted by F. W. Aston, in *Background to Modern Science*, (Eds. J. Needham and W. Pagel), 1938, p. 107. Stas wrote this about 1860-65.

the let-us-suppose variety which could be accepted one day and deposed the next.

Why did Stas become so ardent a follower of Prout in the first place? We may surmise that, as with Faraday, he had faith in the unity of nature and so of matter. But he must have realized, too, that the atomic weights were suggestive of Prout's theory. There must have been a reason why so many of them came near to being multiples of the weight of the hydrogen atom. A broad view of the facts, as they stood, was highly suggestive of the truth of Prout's hypothesis. Today, we should seek to clinch the argument by statistics. Applying this to the results of the atomic weights as Stas determined them, it has been estimated that it is a million-to-one chance that Prout was right. But Stas did not think of this. His results led him to the opposite view, which he adopted with quite unnecessary dogmatism.

The reason was, of course, that a few atomic weights, particularly chlorine which has a value of $35\frac{1}{2}$, did not fit the theory. Stas was faced with a choice. Either (1) he could say that his belief in Prout's theory was correct, but that in some cases unknown factors were interfering with the expected result, or (2) he could say, as in fact he did say, "My theory has caused me to predict the wrong result, therefore my theory must be wrong."

Good Critical Arguments

Our story illustrates a point which is often overlooked. As a rule it is much easier to present a good critical argument than a good constructive one.

The argument which runs: "Since the atomic weight of at least one element involves a half-unit, therefore the elements cannot be built up from hydrogen atoms", sounds extremely convincing. On the other hand, the argument that Prout's theory is right because of the general impression we gain when we look at a list of figures sounds feeble and lacking in proper objectivity. Yet we know that the first argument is wrong, for chlorine is a mixture of isotopes, the atomic weights of which *are* whole numbers, whereas the second argument is overwhelmingly convincing when presented in statistical terms.

Religious Parallel

The story we have told is closely parallelled by the difficulties that sometimes crop up in connection with the Christian faith.

Firstly, let us consider belief in God. Probably everyone who is scientifically inclined has at some time or other been impressed by the grandeur of nature and has felt, in a non-logical way, that it is the work of an Almighty Creator. This argument has appealed overwhelmingly to thinking men in every age and nation. Yet it is difficult, perhaps impossible, to put the argument in a logically watertight form. On the other hand it is easy to argue: "If there is a God, then we should expect the world to be perfect. Since it is not perfect there cannot be a God."

The second argument sounds convincing, but this may only be because destructive arguments are so easily stated. As with Stas's atomic weights, there *may* be an interfering factor. If we judge by its impact upon men of all ages, the really cogent argument is the first—though in our ignorance we cannot express it convincingly.

Humility in Face of Facts

Our analogy clears the ground in another way also. It is sometimes asserted, or implied, that only human pride makes a man doggedly stick to his faith when facts are against him. The humble thing to do is to admit you are wrong. "Sit down before the facts as a little child, be prepared to give up every preconceived notion, follow humbly wherever nature leads, or you will learn nothing"—to quote the well-known words of Thomas Huxley.

This argument is double-edged, and the edge is sharper on the other side. It may well be that Huxley's own singular lack of productive thinking was due to his taking too large a dose of his own medicine. Stas followed humbly where nature led him, right enough, and as a result abandoned his preconceived views. In one sense he demonstrated his humility, but a critic might fairly claim that his change of opinion had more to do with pride than with lowliness of mind. It happened because of his confidence in the logic of his reasoning. Would not a humbler man have been more willing to suspect that an unknown factor was at work? In the same way, a man who abandons his faith in God may do so in the conscious belief that he is humbly bowing before the facts, whilst unconsciously he is proudly asserting that his intellectual grasp of the universe is such that no complicating factors have escaped his notice.

The Bible

Another point concerns the Bible. It is difficult to read the Bible as a whole without an overwhelming conviction that it is a message from God—many of those who call themselves agnostics are willing enough to agree that, at least in the past, it has affected them in this way. But once again it is easy to dissect a verse here and a verse there and to argue: "If this book is true, it will not contradict itself. But the two stories of this and that are not consistent, etc. . . . ." Again, it is the negative argument that is easy to present. We may be quite unable to give a reasoned argument as to why the difficulty is there—any more than Stas could interpret his value of $35\frac{1}{2}$ for chlorine in terms of the theory he so longed to prove. If we make suggestions, they seem baseless and *ad hoc*. But would not Stas have felt the same if a scientific visionary had told him that there *might* be such things as isotopes (atoms of the same element but with different weights)? But again, if the impression comes deeply upon us that God is speaking through the Book, may it not be silly and wrong to cast that early faith aside because of difficulties of this kind?

106

Faith—Supported by Argument?

Now for a further point. It is often said that faith is not a matter for argument. It is claimed by some Christians that it is wrong to try to *prove* any kind of religious belief.[1] Such proofs, we are told, must in the long run do more harm than good. For suppose someone gave you a good proof that God created the universe, that He made life on this planet, or that he worked a certain miracle, and suppose you accepted the proof and believed accordingly. And suppose that, later, a scientist showed that the argument for a creation was invalid, or that life could arise spontaneously, or that the miracle was not a miracle at all but a rare natural event. Then your faith would at once evaporate. And even while you had it your faith would not be worth the having, for it was only a hypothesis and not faith at all. Argument, therefore, it is claimed, is irrelevant to religious faith and must be avoided at all costs.

If this argument is well based, then we have for the first time encountered a valid distinction between scientific and religious faith. For, however deep-rooted scientific faith may be, scientists do not sit back in armchairs proclaiming that it is too sacred to be suscept-

[1] Karl Barth is the best known exponent of this view. See his Gifford Lectures, *The Knowledge of God and the Service of God*, 1938. Kierkegaard was even more violent, According to him, mocking God deliberately "is always preferable to the disparaging air of importance with which one would prove God's existence. For to prove the existence of one who is present is the most shameless affront, since it is an attempt to make him ridiculous". Such views have been admirably discussed and refuted by L. H. de Wolf in his *Religious Revolt against Reason*, 1949.

ible of test in the laboratory. Scientific faith has always been a mainspring for action—science has developed because men have sought to elucidate and confirm some belief after which they were dimly groping in the unconscious. Even the intuitional mathematician is glad to prove his intuitions if he can!

To clear our minds let us imagine ourselves in Stas's shoes. Suppose someone in his day had offered him good statistical evidence of the truth of Prout's theory. Can we even imagine that he would have replied: "I do not want your arguments: I believe implicitly that Prout's law is right and if you start troubling me with arguments my strong faith will degenerate into the status of a hypothesis which I might have to abandon one day if someone came along with another argument in the reverse sense which seemed to me stronger than yours!" The suggestion borders on the ludicrous. Provided he had understood it, he would have accepted the argument with unbounded joy. And a simple argument of this kind would probably have prevented him from making a mistake in later years. It would have enabled him to see clearly that, if a few of the elements did not obey the whole number rule, complicating factors were at work the nature of which he did not understand. Such an argument might even have led him to predict the discovery of isotopes.

If this analogy is sound, we must conclude that it is right and proper to look for arguments in support of religious faith. The pedant may argue to his heart's content that, despite argument, his faith will never

108

really rest on arguments, but it is folly to overlook the fact that argument can prevent the specious undermining of valid faith. This, indeed, is one of its functions. And we must remember that faith of both kinds, scientific and religious, is in fact not infrequently undermined.

There is strong evidence that most people, perhaps all, believe in God in a dim and inarticulate way. Though they cannot put their thoughts into words, they sense that the universe, with all its wonders, is not the product of a blind force, but of an intelligent Almighty Being. (Mass Observation found that 25 per cent. of professed atheists *admit* that they pray to God in trouble,[1] and it is likely that the percentage of those who do so pray, whether they admit it or not, is much higher: Stekel has shown that psychoanalysis likewise affords abundant evidence of a deep-seated belief in God present in those who deny such belief consciously.[2]) They may reject this inner belief deliberately, on account of philosophical difficulties, such as the presence of evil, but it is there none the less. It is most important that they should be helped to bring these inner convictions out into the open. When once we are able, even in a poor way, to see some of the reasons for the

[1] Mass Observation, *Puzzled People*, 1947. The phenomenon of atheist prayer "is an indication of the extent to which agnosticism and atheism fail to penetrate below the expressional verbal surface".

[2] W. Stekel, *The Interpretation of Dreams*, vol. I, 1943. Stekel gives examples of the dreams of atheists which, he is convinced, can only be interpreted as showing a fear of God on account of sins committed. He concludes: "I now see suppressed religion and suppressed morality where I used to see sexual factors of illness".

faith that is in us, we find it easier to realize that we possess the faith.

It is, of course, quite true that arguments are sometimes bad arguments, and that even the best of arguments may appear more convincing at one stage in the world's history, than at another. But this possibility does not absolve us from using the best arguments we can. After all, if Stas had heard a bad argument for Prout's theory which he then or later recognized as bad, it would not have affected the final outcome. On the other hand, if he had heard a good one, he would have remained true to his convictions. Even a bad argument, if he did not know it was bad, might have proved helpful —after all, was it not a bad argument which in the end led him astray? We have already noted how useful logically poor arguments have proved in supporting the faith of such men as Goodyear, Ehrlich and others in their endeavours. Without these arguments, poor as they were, many an investigator would have lost his faith and abandoned his work.

Again, to say that we must not rest on argument but on faith sounds like honest humility. But it is tinged with peevish pride for all that. Who are we to say that unless all the arguments we use are completely unassailable, we shall not use argument at all? How does such an attitude compare with Christ's teaching that if we cannot make use of the single talent, God will not wish to entrust us with many: that if we are not faithful in that which is least, we shall not be trusted with the true riches? What should we think of an astronomer who refused to study the heavens unless the 200-inch telescope was put at his disposal?

It is interesting to note that Kant, who is so often quoted as having proved that no intellectual arguments can demonstrate God's existence, was deeply concerned lest this conclusion should prevent men from using what reason they could to the best of their ability. Speaking of the "proof" from design in nature, he says, "It would therefore be not only extremely sad, but utterly vain, to attempt to diminish the authority of that proof", and again, "But although we have nothing to say against the reasonableness and utility of this line of argument, but wish on the contrary, to commend and encourage it, we cannot approve of the claims which this proof advances of apodictic certainty."[1]

Clarification of Faith

We have noted that argument is valuable because it helps to prevent the undermining of faith. But it has another function too: it often serves to clarify faith. This has proved to be so, especially, in the field of mathematics. Intuitions have often resulted in brilliant discoveries, but prolonged analytical work, whilst confirming the intuitions, has often led to much helpful clarification.

In its beginnings intuition is rarely detailed. A relation is seen to be true—but it is subsequent reasoning which shows the precise conditions in which it will

[1] Immanuel Kant, *Critique of Pure Reason*, trans. by Max Müller, 1881, vol. II, pp. 535-6.

hold. Few generalizations are true under all circumstances.

Faith may tell us that there is truth to be found if we examine a certain question, but it may not tell us exactly what is true in the things that we shall examine. It tells us to dig for gold in such and such a place, but it does not tell us in advance whether all we dig up will be gold, or whether there will be spadefuls of earth as well.

It is the same in religion as in science. It is a matter of common experience that those who refuse to reason about faith are often those who, in the bundle which contains their treasure, retain a good deal of rubbish too. Because they refuse to reason, they cannot learn to discriminate between the treasure and the rubbish. They fear the loss of all if they use their minds. And, of course, there is this to be said in their favour, that it is better to keep the gold with the dross than to lose them both.

Reasoning about faith needs courage. To their credit be it said, scientists have often shown more of this type of courage than have Christians. Religious people, only too often, let the fear of losing the baby with the bathwater dominate their lives. If, in past times, Christians had been more willing to reason, some of the narrower and more unreasonable sects of Christendom would never have arisen. But Christians need hardly be surprised at this situation: as Christ said, the children of this world are, in their generation, wiser than the children of light.

Can Religion be "Proved"

Lastly, something must be said about the use of the word "prove". It is often said that you cannot *prove* God's existence or any item of religious faith. This, of course, is true. But neither can you prove anything at all, except in mathematics, where the proof is, in reality, a restatement of the assumptions you made at the start. The nature of the external world cannot be worked out by logic. We cannot prove the inverse square law or the existence of atoms. We can only look at the facts as we see them and offer what seems to us the best explanation.

In like manner, an argument for the existence of God must always be of the kind: "Here are the facts: is not the natural explanation so-and-so?" Taken in this sense the argument for the main beliefs in Christianity with regard to the origin of the universe, the Plan behind it, the calling of a nation and the coming of the Messiah seem, to the writer at all events, extraordinarily cogent —but this is not the subject of this book.

We must conclude, then, that reason cannot put faith out of business, even when the faith is religious. Faith and reason are allies in religion, just as they are allies in the realm of science.

X

ANALYSING FAITH

Faith Destroyed by Reason?

ON the basis of an analogy, we have reached the conclusion that faith ought, whenever possible, to be supported by reason. But have we not underestimated the dangers? If we analyse faith, to find out whether we possess it, is there not a risk that we shall destroy the faith with which we started?

Stas lost his faith in the unity of matter just because he questioned the evidence upon which it was based. He tried to prove his faith and so lost it. Many people lose their faith in God because, as a result of analysis, they discover that the grounds upon which they hold it are not fully convincing.

When Thinking is Dangerous

To discuss this question, we may begin by noting that, in many simple experiences in everyday life, thinking is sometimes unwise and dangerous. If we keep asking questions about why we believe and act as we do, life becomes difficult or impossible.

This is especially true of skills, habits and instincts. Begin to *think* where the letters are placed on the typewriter keyboard and progress becomes intolerably slow.

Cycle through a busy city and begin to calculate the angle through which you should tilt your machine in order to turn and avoid a collision and you will be lucky to survive. A man who, when asked in court to state what he was doing at such and such a time, would be a fool if he began to ruminate on the number of millilitres of air that he should express from his lungs in order to answer the judge's question.

In man, instinct plays an unimportant role and all or nearly all our disciplines are learned by conscious effort. Often, though not always, the learning stage, which is painfully slow, involves definite thinking about what we do—as in typing or music, for instance. But this may not always be so. Perhaps the toddler, in learning to walk, pays little attention to the complex problem presented by the need to balance himself precariously on two feet. In animals, of course, the need for thought is less than in man and scarcely exists at all. Here most actions are "instinctive"—but though we use this word, it is, of course, a label for ignorance.

It is interesting to note that instincts are compared with faith in the Bible, for example in the Book of Jeremiah. "The stork in the heaven knoweth her appointed times; and the turtle and the swallow and the crane observe the time of their coming, but my people know not the ordinance of the Lord" (Jer. 8.7). The analogy has often appealed to scientifically minded Christians.[1]

---

[1] To William Derham, for example, in his Boyle Lecture, *Physico-theology*, 1713, p. 386.

By reasoning, then, it is possible to alter the thing that is reasoned about. The cycle crashes into the car or the mind loses its spontaneity. Reason may aptly be compared with the ray (strictly *quantum*) of light which we might, in theory, direct upon an electron in order to discover its whereabouts. The reflected ray tells us where the electron *was*, but the act of reflection sends the electron off we know not where.

If, therefore, in our attempts to analyse faith, to prove it or to reason about it in any way whatever, we must necessarily *alter* what we reason about, we can never hope to make headway by reason.

> The centipede was happy—quite!
> Until the toad in fun
> Said, "Pray, which leg moves after which?"
> This raised her doubts to such a pitch,
> She fell exhausted in the ditch,
> Not knowing how to run!

or again,

> He moves upon the water's face
> With ease, celerity and grace;
> But if he ever stopped to think
> Of how he did it, he would sink.
> (Hilaire Belloc, *The Water Spider*)

Analysis may alter what is analysed

Reason can only be profitably applied when this cannot happen. It is reasonable enough to study the tilt of a bicycle *after* traffic has been negotiated or to ask at a later date what the factors were which influenced a certain choice. But we cannot reason about faith, instincts, habits or intuitions at the time that we make use of them. No doubt a part of the reason for this lies in the elementary fact that, when our attention is already fully absorbed by one topic, we cannot be thinking of something else as well.

When applied to the more wonderful and subtle powers of the mind, the use of reason may be really dangerous. A love affair may be ruined if a man and woman are for ever wishing to analyse the precise reasons why they should think they love one another. Analysis of this kind again alters what is being analysed—for intellectual analysis may lead the partners to feel that they do not love one another simply because they do not understand how and why they should.

Experimenters in psychical research have often observed something similar. Thus, in a number of experiments,[1] it is recorded that telepathic results fall off only because the experimenters think that, under the new conditions, telepathy will be harder than before. For example, when the distance is increased, results may fall off simply because there is a semi-conscious feeling that it will be harder to read thoughts at the greater distance. But when the distance is enormously increased, the rational judgment seems to realize its utter uselessness and telepathy is no longer obstructed.

In the same way it is recorded that in premonitions

[1] Eg. J. B. Rhine, *Extra-sensory Perception*, 1935, p. 139 ff.

of danger or death, it sometimes happens that the rational judgment comes in and makes the premonition useless. Instead of accepting a premonition and acting in such a way as to avoid the danger, a man may argue to himself that his fear is silly *because* it is founded on no reasonable basis.[1]

Well-known scientists have drawn attention to the hampering effect of the intellect. Birkhoff, for example, after saying that much that is accepted by mathematicians cannot be proved and that positive faith is necessary for progress, once remarked: "A good many mathematicians are seriously hampered by lack of ardent positive faith . . . This type of deficiency is generally due to a strong development of purely critical powers and to overspecialization."[2] He continued by placing on record the fact that for many years of his life he was unfruitful in discovery because he had allowed himself to become critical in the wrong directions, but added that, when he again began to exert faith, results flowed once more.

In the same vein, W. B. Cannon speaks of research workers he has known who "were so constantly seeing obstacles in their way, and difficulties of interpretation if one or other result might follow from an experimental test" that they could not be induced to commit themselves wholeheartedly to the investigations at hand and so remained unproductive.[3]

[1] For interesting examples of this see A. T. Schofield, *Modern Spiritism*, 1920, pp. 150 ff.
[2] G. D. Birkhoff, *Science*, 1938, **88**, 601.
[3] W. B. Cannon, *op. cit.*, p. 33.

Will Faith Disappear?

We may return to our question. Is it right or wise to examine faith—to seek to prove it, to analyse it, or to try to pull out from the recesses of our minds the reasons why we possess it?

Thus far we have reached the conclusion that if, by so doing, we *alter* the faith we are examining, then we act foolishly and wrongly. But how do we know beforehand whether we shall alter it?

By facing up to this question—suppose I discover, after thinking, that my faith has no discoverable intellectual basis at all, shall I then jump to the conclusion that it is not there?

In fact, of course, faith might well exist without the possiblity of intellectual justification. We have seen that it is possible to receive messages by telepathy and that no amount of introspection or reasoning can tell a man just how or why he knows that so-and-so is thinking of the message he has picked up. Now, if this can happen between men, it can presumably happen also between God and man. Religious faith, then, might be implanted in a similar way by God.[1] And if so, no amount of reasoning would discover why it was there.

There are, then, two points to remember if we use intellect to examine faith. Firstly, we must not ask questions about faith just at the moment when faith ought to be helping us to master some difficulty. For

[1] The suggestion is developed by W. E. Leslie, *Trans. Victoria Institute*, 1924, **56**, 141.

to do so would merely divert attention at a critical time and would alter the situation. Secondly, if we look for the reasons why we hold such-and-such a faith and find none, we must not turn round on our faith and say: "Since I can find no good reason for you, you do not exist!"

Faith—Rational Basis Partial

We have noted that scientific intuition is often partly rational and partly beyond reason. It is natural, then, to suppose that the same is true of religious faith also. If so, when we look for the grounds of religious faith, we shall probably find some at least—though there will certainly be a large element which cannot be logically explained. But even of the part that *can* be put in logically reasoned form, it is likely that much will escape our notice—Stas completely overlooked a strong intellectual argument in support of his faith.

Discovering a reason for the faith that we hold is no easy matter. In some instances it has taken mathematicians centuries to prove results which were obtained first of all intuitively. There is depth beyond depth in the unconscious of all of us—we cannot seriously hope to plumb those depths in a hurry. So at best the results of a search for the reasons for faith are likely to be superficial.

All this implies that any trace of pride in our powers to analyse faith is fraught with danger. Since at best we can hope to discover but little, we must learn the meaning of humility. The chief danger does not lie

in asking questions but in the pride that is content with superficial answers.

We may compare the situation with attempts to reason about Biblical miracles. To say that the walls of Jericho fell down as a result of an earthquake (assuming this to be proved) is to explain the event at a certain level. And the explanation is well worth advancing for it makes the story credible and encourages faith. Yet the deeper problem—why did the earthquake occur just when it did?—is left untouched. The problem is pushed back a stage rather than solved.

In the same way, if we are psychologically minded, we may make suggestions about the nature of intuition. It is due, perhaps, to the workings of the unconscious mind.[1] Perhaps this is true in part, but it would be trivial and flippant to assert that the mystery was solved—especially as no one has ever proved that this hypothesis is true, nor are they likely ever to do so. All we can say is that ideas start at "the fringe of consciousness" and that the process of making them conscious does not, apparently, differ much from one individual to another. Perhaps some ideas are implanted in the unconscious by God, others we pick up by telepathy

[1] This hypothesis is worked out by Poincaré, Hadamard, Beveridge and others. In one of Poincaré's inspirations the new insight was "not of the same nature as the previous conscious work". This is suggestive of another mind at work. The mathematician Cardan, like Plato in ancient days, seems to have sensed a mysterious voice telling him what to investigate. Such facts *suggest* that minds other than our own may sometimes be at work, but in view of the possibility of split-personality (cf. Morton Prince's well-known work on the Sally-Beauchamp case in his *Dissociation of a Personality*, 1906) they certainly do not prove it.

from other people and yet others are worked out by the unconscious mind. These possibilities do not exclude one another—an idea picked up, for example, by telepathy, might need working out before it became conscious.

To dismiss a problem because it has been superficially explained is to be guilty of inexcusable conceit. In the long run such pride makes men incapable of any kind of thinking at its deepest level—either in science or religion. Unless we have the humility to look at problems from new angles we shall never travel far on the road to understanding anything, however partially.

Explaining and Explaining Away

A common habit, now fortunately on the decline, is to explain things in terms of origins. But explaining is not explaining away. A man's religious faith may be "explained" on the basis of the teaching he received as a child, but it is none the worse for its lowly beginnings. We do not refuse to take chemistry seriously because, historically, it had roots in alchemy, nor astronomy because it started with astrology. Nor are the wisest living men any the worse for the fact that they are grown-up babies. No more is faith unreal because, for all we can remember, its first conscious glimmerings began when a mother told a child about a Father in heaven and the child responded by picturing God as the "projection of the parent."

Far from explaining faith away, such "explanations" (assuming them to be true) are fully consistent with the

view that certain basic experiences in the lives of all of us helped us to realize and articulate truths which were already present in our developing minds. In a similar way, the history of religion may show, not that Christianity is false because there are features common to it and to pagan religions, but that through the ages man's mind was slowly groping after truth or, alternatively, that God was beginning to reveal Himself in pre-Christian times.

Communication of Faith

Analysis of faith, then, is not wrong in principle. Though it will never reveal fully why or how faith is held, it may bring to light some of its more superficial aspects. These may be of great value in communicating faith to others. Despite their poverty of expression, to speak of them may serve to help other people to focus attention upon a faith of which they are only dimly aware. Faraday sensed a relation between magnetism and electricity: he *knew* he was right but he could not communicate his faith to others until he had discovered how to do an experiment which would prove his point. The mathematician dimly sees that a certain relation holds; only after he has dragged a proof out of his subconscious (if this is the correct description of what he does) can he pass it on to others.

In the same spirit the Bible urges Christians so far as they are able, to give a reason for the faith that is in them: "Being ready always to give answer to every man that asketh you a reason for the hope that is in you, yet with meekness and fear" (1 Pet. 3.15). The passage contrasts strangely with the "boldness" which was so characteristic of early Christian preaching ("They spake the word of God with boldness"—Acts 4.31, etc.), but we can undestand why. When you have worked out the reason for your faith as well as you can, the reasons you have found may only be superficial ones and they may even be wrong ones. So of course "meekness and fear" ("gentleness and reverence" RSV)—not arrogance and dogmatism—is the quality called for.

XI

FAITH AND SOCIETY

Discovery—The Enemy of Society

DESPITE the compelling nature of the evidence, the mere mention of the need for the exercise of faith in science sometimes acts like the traditional red rag to the traditional bull. Amongst Rationalists, in particular, there seems to be a general understanding that the role of faith should be suppressed or minimized.

The reason for this is not far to seek. Once admit the necessity of faith, once begin to honour and respect the innovator, and what have you? A world full of cranks and enthusiasts, of ignorant men setting themselves up above the specialists! For who is to judge which man's faith is the genuine article? How can the true scientist—or saint for that matter—be identified in the midst of a host of enthusiasts and rogues?

This is a very real difficulty. Yet we must be clear from the start that the existence of the difficulty in no way affects the fact that faith is vitally necessary. We cannot conjure faith out of existence merely because it raises awkward problems. Besides, we have already noted that, if the human mind were made in such a way that faith was unnecessary, other perhaps even more forbidding difficulties would have to be faced.

Faith, then, is vital, and yet its existence is a menace to established science and to society in general. Without faith there can be no great discoveries and science stagnates. But great discoveries upset the *status quo* and disturb everyone.[1]

Innovation in Religion

The dilemma is the same for religion as for science. Established religion, like established science, finds new ideas difficult to assimilate, dangerous, and revolutionary. Israel persecuted the prophets in ancient times and the Church continued the persecution in the Middle Ages. There is no objective standard by which an established scientific or religious hierarchy can determine which innovators have a valuable message to pass on and which are mere enthusiasts. The former, like the latter, appear foolish, as we have already noted. As a result, Christians with a message, like scientific discoverers, tend to find themselves outcasts.

It has often been pointed out by religious writers that, in each generation, those who have spiritual insight have usually, if not always, arisen from the poorer classes, despised by the influential, the rich, and the powerful.[2] It is amongst the sects and minorities of the

[1] The theme is developed by Darlington, *op. cit.*

[2] E. Tröltsch, *The Social Teachings of the Christian Church*, vol. I, p. 44. Tröltsch uses the significant words ". . . who have not acquired the habit of intellectual reasoning". In this connection E. H. Broadbent's *The Pilgrim Church*, 1935, is well worth reading despite its somewhat extreme attitude.

past that we must look for effective protest against such evils as the crusades, the slave trade, the suffering of the labouring classes, the shameful conditions of the prisons or the sinfulness of war. Powerful religious groups always favour the *status quo*: they follow public opinion instead of leading it.

Hypocrisy

It is for this reason that, viewed from outside, Christianity often seems hypocritical and failing in its mission. But there is nothing surprising in this. It arises because of the very nature of our minds—the way in which God has made them. It is inevitable that those with experience, ripe judgment and knowledge should rise to the top. Could we wish it otherwise? It is also inevitable that the characteristics we have mentioned, unfit men to see new light themselves or to appreciate the insights of others. Inevitably leaders oppose innovators. Even when the leaders are men who had new insights themselves when young and suffered for their faith, they will often cause the same suffering to others when they have become old and established.

It is not religion which makes hypocrites of men: any organized system does the same. Only a few saintly people will escape the charge and saintly people— Faraday is the best known example in science—often eschew leadership and administration. Science and religion alike illustrate the truth of the words of Christ: "The last shall be first and the first last."

Our Lord told the Pharisees that they built the

tombs of the prophets and proclaimed that if they had lived in former days they would not have soiled their hands with the blood of God's saints. Yet in their own day these hypocrites filled up the measure of their fathers' sins by doing the same things—persecuting those whose spiritual vision was nobler than their own (Matt. 23.29 ff.; Luke 2.39 ff.). And this, too, is exactly what every generation of scientists has done. They praise the brilliant scientists of the past, celebrating their centenaries if not decorating their tombs, but at the same time opposing those with fresh outlooks in their own day.[1] Biographies of scientists are frequently written in the spirit of "if we had lived in the days of our fathers, we should not have persecuted the prophets." But we may be certain that the same treatment is even now being meted out to thousands of unknown scientific "prophets" possessed of vision and faith. And what science has done the Church also has done down the years. Yet Christ taught, and the scientific biographer takes the same view, that few human sins are more heinous than the sin of the man in position and power who denies to the younger man the right to be heard, when there is something new and important that needs to be said.

Evils of Science

It is easy for men in the modern age to declare that religion has been a menace down the ages because it

[1] For examples see R. H. Murray, *op. cit.* and J. Y. Simpson, *Landmarks in the Struggle between Science and Religion*, 1925.

has persecuted minorities and filled the earth with blood. Considering how short a time organized science has been with us, the evils wrought in its name compare most unfavourably with those wrought in the name of religion—horrible as these have often been.

Within living memory science has inculcated human pride as flagrant as anything of which religion may be ashamed. We read of Archimedes boasting that, given a lever and something on which its fulcrum might rest, he could move the world. The same attitude— the same lust for power—feeds upon and is in turn fed by science. Men forge ahead with the technological aspirations of their countries, ignoring the social evils and suffering caused. Men may die by the millions —as they did in the collectivisation of the farms in Russia after the Revolution—but what matters? It is part of the price which must be paid for the brave new world of tomorrow. Or animals are tortured and slaughtered by the thousand not, indeed, to discover urgently needed medical knowledge which might help both animals and men in their fight against disease, but merely to test the effectiveness of new means for scientific butchery in war.

The discovery of explosives, of the internal combustion engine, of atomic energy and even of poison gases have all been of great value to mankind, but each has brought in its train a host of evils—fear, devastation, wars and rumours of war. We may say, if we choose, that scientists are not responsible for the uses to which their discoveries are put, or that the mischief is the fault of the pseudo-scientist rather than the scientist, but to say these things is only to say that scientists are not *specially* blameworthy above other men. It can scarcely be doubted that men in general, including scientists, are responsible for the evils that they do. The resulting suffering and devastation is not less than that which has accrued from bigoted religious beliefs in past ages. Probably it is more.

Often individual scientists, like individual Popes and bishops, have been much to blame. After World War II, Heisenberg is reported to have said, "In the summer of 1939 twelve people might still have been able, by coming to mutual agreement, to prevent the construction of atom bombs". Dr Robert Jungk asks why Heisenberg himself, with Fermi, did not take the initiative instead of letting the opportunity slip by. "Their powers of political and moral indignation," he concluded, "failed them at that moment as disastrously as did their loyalty to the international tradition of science."[1]

Of course, most individual Christians were *not* responsible for what happened in the past, just as most scientists are not individually responsible for scientific evils today. And again, it was pseudo-Christians, misusing religious truths, who did most of the damage in the past, just as it is the pseudo-scientists who are most blameworthy today.

But to continue, Nazi scientists actually used human beings as guinea-pigs. Frequently they even used their

[1] R. Jungk, *Brighter than a Thousand Suns*, 1958.

130

victims indiscriminately and irresponsibly, killing hundreds when only a few (horrible as is even this) would have sufficed.[1]

It will not do to blame politicians for distorting science, for the influence is two-wayed. Bad politicians are made worse by scientific theories and may even be created by them. Darwin's theory captured the imagination of the youthful Hitler long before he was in a position to make the universities toe the party line in science. Karl Marx even wished to dedicate his book *Das Kapital* to Darwin.[2]

Anti-Theological Prejudice

In Russia the same intolerance, often resulting in murder and concentration camp for scientists with unacceptable scientific beliefs, is again only too familiar. Here the only science allowed is materialistic. Those who held scientific views in physics, biology (especially genetics), chemistry (for example the resonance theory), psychology, and astronomy, which seemed to lend themselves to the "idealism" of the West, were, until recently at all events, ruthlessly persecuted. In Russian orthodoxy one of the chief objects of science is to kill religion; and when, as often happens, science lends support to religious beliefs it is the scientists with the insight to see it and the courage to say it who have to

[1] For a brief summary see A. C. Laennec, *Medical Experimentation on Man*, Eng. trans., 1955, pt. IV.

[2] See J. M. Barzun, *Darwin, Marx and Wagner*, 1942, also the author's *Darwin: Before and After*, 1948 and 1958.

suffer. No one who has studied the genetics controversy of a few years back can fail to see the meaning of events.

The Russians were fearful lest a belief in genes would put theology on the map, and they said so again and again. Zhdanov publicly apologized to Stalin for having formerly held "these anti-scientific views . . . which in theory are a veiled form of clericalism—theological concepts of the origin of species as the result of individual acts of creation". The fact that Mendel and Malthus were priests was referred to again and again and taken as proof that their theories, in some way, favoured theology. Those who sought to defend the Western views were driven to the argument that belief in genes did not favour theology after all. Prezent gave the game away when he said: "Nobody will be led astray by the Morganists' false analogies between the invisible atom and the invisible gene. *Far closer would be an analogy between the invisible gene and the invisible spirit.*"[1]

But we do not have to travel to the ends of the earth to see scientific hypocrisy at work. Rationalist writers are for ever eulogizing the scientific attitude. They know as well as we do that the true scientific attitude is like the true Christian attitude—the attitude of mind which makes intuition possible and faith a reality. But they write and speak as if science stands for a cold,

[1] *The Situation in Biological Science: Proceedings of the Lenin Academy of Agricultural Sciences of the U.S.S.R.*, Moskow (Eng. trans.), 1948, p. 602. At a later date the view that genes are compatible with atheism after all was accepted in Russia. But in 1958 Prezent was gaining power once more.

objective and rational attitude. Does talk of this kind suggest sincerity of heart to an impartial observer?

Those who make science their god urge that education should be so devised as to help the young to think creatively. But how often is any kind of instruction given in science courses which might enable students at least to know how the great discoveries of the past were made? Though nations look to science to help them in years to come they make no serious attempt at all to discover how science advances. Saccharin was not discovered by trying to improve sugar, nor aniline dyes by trying to improve natural ones.[1] "Everyone knows that electric light was not invented through trying to improve candles, but everyone, or nearly everyone, acts as though it had been", writes Darlington.[2] We train the future generation to add scraps of knowledge to the knowledge already known—but is there no hypocrisy in ignoring the more important issues, especially when we know that it is fear of the consequences which prevents the encouragement of originality?

Indeed, the charge of hypocrisy has been openly levelled against the planners of science who ignore the known facts about discovery in their ardent zeal to set up vast laboratories which will turn out scientific results like sausages from sausage machines. "The planners adopt a pharisaical air of ethical superiority," complains J. R. Baker. "They presume to give the

[1] J. R. Baker, *The Scientific Life*, 1942, chap. 5.
[2] C. D. Darlington, *op. cit.*

impression that they alone are concerned with the welfare of humanity, while other scientists study nothing but their own inclinations and convenience."[1]

Science and Private Life

Today countless numbers trust in science rather than in religion. But it has been well remarked that though science has proved one thing after another, people go on living as if the science in which they profess to believe had thrown no light whatever on the effects of bad human habits.[2] Scientific knowledge on the effects of alcoholism does not stop people drinking more than is good for them: scientific knowledge on the effects of over-eating does not prevent obesity; scientific studies linking many physical ailments with wrong psychological attitudes and, often, with what Christians call definite acts of sin, does not make men peaceful and virtuous; there is no evidence that social science makes men socially minded. When scientific results are unwelcome, their significance is dwindled down by a casuistry which matches anything of which the Jesuits were guilty (Chapter 7). Scientists and believers in science generally are not less hypocritical than church people. More often than not those who object to religion because they prefer a "scientific attitude", do not permit their science to penetrate to their private lives.

[1] J. R. Baker, op. cit., p. 6. In their analysis of modern inventions Jewkes et al (op. cit.) find that the great nations with large industrial research organizations do not produce a larger output of new inventions than nations not possessed of these advantages.

[2] M. G. Mellon, Science, 1943, 97, 362.

Another example of the hypocrisy to which science so easily leads was pointed out some years ago by C. L. Bryant. It is a stock-in-trade argument among rationalists that Christians in foreign lands often uproot the culture that they find and put nothing in its place—the implication being that missionary work does more harm than good. It is conveniently overlooked that science has a precisely similar effect upon modern man. Too often it uproots his religious belief but puts nothing in its place. Those who use the first argument reveal their prejudice in that they do not oppose the teaching of science on the same grounds.

Faith—Good and Bad

The conclusion is clear. Science, like religion, is easily abused and the same human failings are to be found in both movements. But this is no argument against science as such, or against religion as such. Science in itself is good and Christianity is good, however much they both may have been perverted.

The plain fact is that faith is always a dangerous thing. But all the best things in life are dangerous—more dangerous the more valuable and wonderful they are. The eating of good food may lead to gluttony; sex, which should foster tenderness, love and happiness, can also destroy them. It is hardly surprising if faith, perhaps the noblest endowment of all, can become man's greatest enemy. Neither science nor religion can do without it, but a blind and intolerant faith in science or in religion may do much harm, becoming a scourge of history. "We are very apt all of us to call that faith, that perhaps may be but carnal imagination, and carnal reasonings" said Oliver Cromwell.

How then can a man know that that in which he puts his faith is right?

There is no slick and easy answer here. But the question, of course, is badly framed, for the man who has faith *does know*. That is just the danger. For what he knows or thinks he knows may be untrue and even wicked. And just because he has faith he is almost (though not quite) incapable of recognizing the fact.

The story of the development of science is bogged down with false faith. Men have held tenaciously to false hypotheses, confusing them with faith. So resistant to change have they become that, on many occasions, further advance has been impeded until an older generation has died out and been replaced by a younger.

Christians, like scientists, are well aware of the difficulties—well aware of the fact that men often possess faith which leads them astray. Jesus said as much when He warned His disciples that the time would come when those who murdered them would imagine that they were doing God a service. He warns us that what we take to be the light of faith may, in reality, be darkness (Luke 11.35).

Test of Faith

What will the scientist say if we ask him how to guard against this possibility? Firstly he will say that there is no foolproof recipe known to man. But, having said that, he will probably tell us that our minds must be peaceful, unhurried, earnest, sincere and, above all, fearless. If you have a repressed fear lest, if faith should carry you in such and such a direction, you will be a social outcast or that the equilibrium of your life will be upset in some way, then you will probably never be capable of sound faith in that direction. Your real object must be to find the truth or solve the problem for the love of it and not because you want to establish your reputation in the scientific world. If an intuition comes to you and you find that it makes you proud instead of humble, or if you find yourself apt to push it down the throats of others who are not ready for it, you should look at it again, for it may be false or contain elements of falsehood. You must, too, have a sense of adventure—the feeling that you are alone in the universe, away from your fellow men, in direct contact with nature (or God) and freed for a while from the chains of thought that bind you in your normal life.

If faith comes to you after you have obeyed all these conditions with sincerity of mind, then you may hope that your faith is sound, true and healthy. Yet with all this you *may* go wrong, for the thoughts of the mind are so difficult and subtle that none of us can be quite sure of his own complete integrity (we have much to learn from the psychoanalysts here). And often, perhaps, we set ourselves tasks far beyond anything for which we have the necessary intellectual equipment, so that the generalizations upon which we set our trust may be mere superficialites.

Perhaps all scientists would agree with most if not all of this statement. And in every point it is parallelled by the teaching of the New Testament. Jesus taught that those who were sincerely willing to do God's will would *know* whether his teaching was true or not—they would find that the seed of faith was sown in their hearts. The need for peacefulness of mind and earnestness in seeking after truth is repeatedly emphasized. The need to seek the praise that comes from God only rather than that which comes from men—the worldly reputation—and the teaching that we must be humble for God resists the proud (and in the end makes a fool of him) is all there in the Bible. The need for a sense of loneliness with God and our responsibility to Him and to Him alone for the opinions we hold and the way we direct our lives is emphasized; but we are taught also that, when we have done what we sincerely think is our best, even then we *may* be wrong. "I know nothing against myself, yet am I not hereby justified but he who judges me is the Lord," says St Paul. All this is common to religious and to scientific faith, both taken at their best.

It was said of Michael Faraday that, in some mysterious way, "he smelled the truth". In the same way a person who heeds the conditions should instinctively arrive at religious truth.

XII

HOW CAN A MAN BELIEVE?

WE have examined the arguments which are supposed to prove that religious faith is out of touch with the modern mode of thought. Without exception we have discovered that, in fact, these very arguments prove the opposite to be true. There is little or nothing to be said about Christian faith, so far as it affects what a man must do, but what is already familiar to us through science.

Faith in Fields other than Science

Now although we have drawn our analogies from the domain of science, a physician might have drawn them from medicine, an historian from history, an artist from art, a musician from music or a professor of English from literature.[1] It would be easy to quote great artists, musicians and writers to the effect that what they created was not in reality their own but was given them in moments of inspiration. Blake, Milton, Dickens, Thackeray, Coleridge, and many others among great writers, have described such inspirations. Often

---

[1] The best general reference is B. Ghiselin (Ed.), *The Creative Process, a Symposium* (Univ. of California Press), 1952. See also Harding *op. cit,*, and E. Densmore's Introduction to H. Tuttle's *Arcana of Nature*, 1909, etc.

they commenced to write without knowing what they were about to write or even being fully aware of what they were writing; or they dreamed the stories of their novels or the words of their poems and quickly committed them to paper on waking. Science is not alone in its dependence upon faith and inspiration.

Hunches are not Rare

Now, although few of us can hope to make great discoveries there is no reason to doubt that we can all use our minds in the way that the discoverer does. Of the chemists who replied to the Platt and Baker questionnaire, no less than 83 per cent. said that they had experienced hunches. Blake used to tell his friends that they had the same power as he if only they would cultivate it: "You have only to work up imagination to the state of vision and the thing is done." And it is likely that, in the ordinary affairs of life, when problems prove perplexing or when frustrations have to be faced, most people do, at times, solve problems in this way.

Turning to the Bible, we often read that Jesus, whilst on earth, was filled with amazement. There is no suggestion that He was surprised at the selfishness, immorality and cruelty of men—what amazed Him was man's lack of faith. Faith is the endowment that distinguishes man from the animals. But too often men do not cultivate it. This is the amazing thing, for it is man's most precious gift. Without it, life is pointless, dull and meaningless. And God, in His wisdom, so the Bible teaches, decided to give the gift of salvation not to the rich and influential, not to doers of good works *per se*, not to those endowed with favourable genes or blessed with a good environment, but to those who exercise faith. For this is what everybody can do.

Analogies in the Bible

In the Bible the exercise of faith in ordinary life— the sudden flash of intuition with which a new idea dawns, followed by the effort and devotion necessary to bring the idea to fruition—is freely compared with religious faith.

The point is forcifully put in the third chapter of St John's Gospel where Jesus compares conversion to a new birth. "Marvel not that I said unto thee, Ye must be born anew (=from above?). The wind bloweth where it listeth, and thou hearest the voice thereof, but knowest not whence it cometh or whither it goeth: so is every one that is born of the spirit." Conversion means (or at least includes) accepting a new idea about God. This new insight comes in a way that is beyond our understanding—like the unexpected gust of wind, we cannot tell where it started or what happens to it later, but we feel its impact suddenly and unexpectedly.

This is how faith is born. But Nicodemus, to whom our Lord was speaking, failed to see the point, so Jesus said to him, in effect: "I am merely telling you about what I and my disciples have seen daily as the multitudes turn to God. You have just called me a Teacher come from God. Very well then—I am now telling you of a mere *earthly* thing—a simple fact about how people receive new truth. Art thou a teacher in Israel and knowest not these things? If you disbelieve me, now, it will be of little good if I tell you of *heavenly* things! ..."

In several of the parables (Matt. 13) the point is the same. Ideas concerning the kingdom are thrown out like seed by the sower and, psychologically, their fate is like that of other radically new ideas which enter the minds of men. The parables of the Treasure in the Field and of the Pearl Merchant likewise clearly draw a comparison between radically new secular ideas and Christian truth. In the eleventh chapter of Hebrews we have many examples of how *ideas* of things not seen as yet led men to various kinds of activity. Had the Bible been written in our day, we cannot doubt but that much of its teaching would have been aptly illustrated by analogies drawn from contemporary science and industry.

The Command to Believe

In the New Testament command, "Believe and thou shalt be saved", we see, then, not an impossible command concerning something outside the experience of modern man, but a command that we should use the powers with which we are endowed on the serious issues of our relationship to God and the universe around us. The scientist uses these powers freely in making discoveries about nature: musicians, artists, writers use them in other directions. It is reasonable and right that we should all use them in relation to the most serious problems of all.

How then shall we set about finding religious faith—
supposing we lack it? Again we shall take the cue from
science. Looking back, especially to Chapter 3, we note
that discovery usually starts with some challenging and
puzzling problem.

The field of enquiry out of which religion is born is
certainly of this challenging kind. Let us enumerate
some of the puzzling problems. What is the meaning of
existence? Why are we here? Can we imagine that, after
a life's work, we shall simply disappear into nothingness?

Science poses Problems

Far from making it hard for modern man to face such
issues, science makes them more pressing and focuses
attention upon them. We see ourselves as minute
midgets on a little planet which has circled around a
star a few thousand million times in all. We come and
are gone within less than a mere hundred of these
journeys—like flowers of the field we blossom and die.
Even the star which we call the sun is but one amidst
quadrillions—seemingly no more important than a
single grain of sand chosen at random from all the sea-
shores of the world, or a single straw from all the world's
haystacks. Yet the odd thing is that we—these tiny
midgets—seem alone in understanding this. Cats, birds
and ants do not think about galaxies and atoms.

The results of astronomical research, taken alone,
give us a sense of isolation and loneliness. If we think
of ourselves as living on a little raft in an ocean of space,
doomed to live and die within a mere moment of cosmic

time, how can we know that truth and goodness are important? Thinking along these lines, may we not well conclude that there is "no land to go to, no boats to pick us up, nothing to expect from death and nothing for our plucky little band to do but to be comfortable and intelligent."[1] For most of us, at least, such conclusions are absurd and only religion can preserve sane thinking.

Such considerations lead us to the next problem. Despite all that a too critical reason may say, we can scarcely help accepting the Christian values—in theory at least. We know very well that we have often fallen short of the standards which we accept. Deciding to be better in future does not wipe out the memory of the past, and too often we find that, despite good resolutions, we have no power to mend our ways. In addition, we may be aware that we have set our standards too low.

This is one side of the story. Are there any hints which would seem to point a way out of the dilemma?

Undoubtedly there are. It is hard to believe that the vastness and grandeur of nature is *all* a matter of chance. It is hard to believe that we are the *only* thinking creatures when we can see, all around us, signs of wonderful and elaborate mechanisms which look as if they had been planned. Are the properties of the chemical elements just a matter of chance too—carbon, nitrogen, oxygen and the rest? Are the remarkable properties of water and carbon dioxide again due

[1] The quotation is from A. H. Dakin's useful book, *Man the Measure, an Essay on Humanism as Religion*, 1939, p. 84.

to chance? There is much here that cannot be explained away by a doctrine of the survival of the fittest nor by any other known scientific theory.

Again, the wonder, beauty and complexity of the world suggest that it is wrong to gauge importance merely by a consideration of relative size. Man's body may be small, astronomically speaking, but his power to think about the universe makes him unique. And even the argument from smallness meets its scientific counterpart—for man is gigantic indeed, chemically speaking. Ten thousand million million million million atoms arranged in a miracle of organization!

Man's Reaction to the Problem of Life

Yet again, is science pointing to an unknown God? Even the most atheistic scientist will never crack a joke about what is behind nature. The never-ending series of undreamed-of discoveries seem, almost against man's will, to demand a sense of reverence. What is the meaning of nature? What is behind it?

Every now and again—with some of us very rarely, with others quite often—there comes into our minds a sudden feeling of reverence. It often comes while we are deeply impressed by the sight of some beautiful scenery—it may even come for no obvious reason at all. There comes at such times the sense that we are not alone. There is contact of some kind with the universe —but no descriptive words seem adequate to describe what it is that happens. A scientist will not infrequently experience this "intimate feeling of communion with nature"[1] when, in a flash of understanding, he obtains a new insight. Such an experience may well be the beginnings of contact with a Person greater and wiser than we, but loving and understanding. Perhaps the relationship between this experience and discovery is due to the fact that, in discovering scientific truth, a man uses his mind in the same way as he must use it if he would find God. At such times he is not far from the kingdom of heaven. This experience is associated with no drugged or sleepy state of mind, but rather it is the height of awareness. Our minds are functioning at their best: not at their worst. The experience passes—but it leaves a sacred memory. It is difficult to resist the conviction that it has something to do with the mystery of existence.

In the Bible we find yet another pointer. Whether we like it or no, it is very hard *not* to believe that Jesus of Nazareth had something to do with man's problem. However muddled we may feel about the creeds of the Church, it is difficult to read the story of the life of Jesus without believing that He had solved the great enigma and that He was in some unique way connected with God—if there be a God. Statements of the kind: "I am the way, the truth and the life", "No man cometh unto the Father but by me" and "I have overcome the world" (spoken on the eve of His death!) are awe-inspiring—to say the least. Whatever good we may find in other great world-religions, there is nothing in them to compare with Jesus of Nazareth.

[1] R. S. Mulliken, *Science*, 1937, **86**, 65.

There is plenty to puzzle and concern us in these and a host of other questions and perplexities. If we are to live happily with a sense of purpose, we must make sense of man's place in the world. To do so must become a vital concern.

"Good Soil"

But this is not all. We have seen how the great discoverers have turned again and again to a problem which they could not at first solve. We must be prepared to do the same. This is, in fact, a test of our sincerity. The man who gives a matter up after a few tries shows no sense of perseverence or earnestness. He is treating faith—the faith that in the end light and understanding will dawn—as if it were hypothesis.

This point is brought out by our Lord in the parable of the sower. It is the "good soil" only which gives a harvest—the soil well tilled and prepared. Psychological conversions can nearly always be engineered[1] and may be accompanied by much emotion (". . . immediately receives it with joy"—Matt. 13.20). Though we cannot plant the seeds of truth, we can and should prepare our minds to be receptive and responsive to those seeds of thought that come our way. We have seen that one way of doing this is to return over and over again to a problem that baffles us.

Sincerity is vital. We cannot imagine a scientific discovery being made by a person who, at the back of

[1] See W. Sargent, *Battle for the Mind; a Physiology of Conversion and Brain-washing*, 1957.

147

his mind, rather hopes that anything he may discover will not shatter his prestige, or by one who feels that it would be too much trouble to develop his ideas anyway.

When a man sets out insincerely, without counting the cost, any discoveries he may make are as likely to be false as true. There is a good deal about this sinister possibility in the Bible as, indeed, we have already noted. A lying spirit entered the prophets who merely wished to please King Ahab. There is a broad way that leads to destruction, and those who go in thereby are those who seek excuses why they should not do God's will when they know it. Because of their sins God sends upon men a working of delusion that they should believe a lie.

Prejudices

We learned in Chapter 7 that prejudice easily blinds people to the significance of facts with which they are well acquainted. What, then, are the main prejudices against which we should be on our guard?

One of them, undoubtedly, is reluctance to admit that we are not as clever as we should like to imagine. We see this prejudice at work in the scientist who does not tell, at the time, how his ideas come to him. Kekulé waited till he was an old man before divulging the true source of his inspiration—he waited, in fact, until there was no longer a risk that men would laugh. We tend to glorify our intellects and are secretly ashamed of the fact that our best ideas come from dreams, from hunches, from illogical reasoning and apparently worthless analogies. Scientists tend to hide this fact and to put forward their beliefs in a logical form which cannot easily be controverted. When they describe a discovery they keep "the ideas which gave it birth concealed like the works of a clock behind a clock-face."[1] Or again, as Beveridge (speaking of scientific memoirs in general) puts it: "The logical presentation of results which is usually followed is hardly ever a chronological or full account of how the investigation was actually carried out."[2]

Religion brings this shame into the open. If you become a Christian you can no longer pretend to yourself and others that your reason is enough. You cannot express your faith in a purely logical way: you cannot verify the predictions made on the basis of your discovery by actual observation. Not, at least, in this present age. If you have what seems to you a brilliant idea, you cannot write a paper on it, or claim that it is original. No one will look to you as its inventor or discoverer. In fact, they may think you a fool.

And if becoming a Christian means that we are confessing, in effect, the poverty of our reason, we make the same confession, even more obviously, in regard to our morals. We admit that we are imperfect. Otherwise there would be little point in looking to Christ for aid. "I came not to call the righteous but sinners to repentance."

[1] A. H. Read, *A Sign-post to Mathematics*, 1951.
[2] Beveridge, *op. cit.*, p. 83.

For the older and more experienced person, the humiliating nature of Christianity, like that of science, is seen also in the fact that, despite years of thought and effort, the young upstart may discover, without difficulty, truths hidden from the wise. Jews were furious when Jesus pressed home the point that God had often helped mere heathen Gentiles instead of privileged Israelites (Luke 4.25 ff.). In a parable He told of how men, employed at the last hour of the day, were rewarded equally with those who had toiled since the rising of the sun (Matt. 20). In religion, as in science, it is hard for the rich and clever to take their place with the poor and ignorant.

In the Bible a moment of decision is taken for granted. Insight is gained in a sudden hunch, but soon after there comes the temptation to let the subject drop. The labour involved may seem too great or the cares and pleasures of the world may swamp the new understanding (in the parable, the seed that has hardly begun to sprout), so that it becomes unfruitful. This is why revivalist techniques are often so disappointing. If you have sought passionately for insight, you will appreciate the light when it comes; but if it comes unasked, or is thrust upon you by others, you may not realize its worth.

To all this science offers parallels. You cannot accept a radically new idea without a moment of decision in which you have to decide whether to reject the idea or to accept it. If you accept it, you may feel remorse that you were so foolish as not to have seen it before. And the new idea will be sure to make demands on you. It must be brought to the notice of others: you will feel the challenge to vindicate the step you have taken. But if your search for the truth that now seems within your grasp was not sufficiently earnest, you will be tempted to let the matter drop.

Lack of Novelty in Religion?

At first sight it may seem that intuitions in religion differ from those in science in that they are not new. But this difference is unreal. Many discoveries in science and ways of doing things in technology have been repeatedly rediscovered again and again. And there is a sense of adventure, too, in entering into the discoveries of others. The more we have struggled to solve some problem, the greater the joy we experience when we grasp the solution. Coulson[1] aptly reminds us of how, in 1913, N. R. Campbell had just finished revising a book on Modern Electrical Theory. He chanced to glance at a paper by Niels Bohr, of whom he had never previously heard, and "in half an hour I was in a state of excitement and exctasy, such as I have never experienced before or since in my scientific career . . . Twenty years have not damped my enthusiasm." Here, as in all other such cases, Campbell's enthusiasm and joy were due in no small measure to the fact that he had been groping after the idea which Bohr had found. It is the same in religion. A truth, when it dawns upon

[1] C. A. Coulson, *op. cit.*, p. 50. See Campbell's Obituary Notice, *Proc. Physical Soc.*, 1949, **162**, 857.

us, is not less a personal discovery of our very own, because others have found it first. It is of small moment whether an idea is ultimately original or not: the real risk is that we may accept a ready-made religion (or scientific theory) blindly, before our minds contain the well-tilled soil in which it can grow.

Creeds

This helps us to understand why theology is so often a hurdle in the path of the would-be Christian. We may well imagine the joy that early Christians felt when, after years of perplexity, they formulated creeds which seemed to express truths held hazily beforehand. But the dead hand of time has fallen upon their formulations. Today creeds seem to say: "If you discover anything, you *must* discover it just so!" Yet we surmise that if we decide beforehand what a discovery will be like, it will be no discovery at all.

If we are to know the thrill of discovering Christianity afresh, it must be because there is some personal discovery for us to make. Though the kernel is the same no two people discover it in just the same way. Every Christian believes that Christ's death has something to do with the forgiveness of his sins, but Christians down the ages have expressed this conviction very differently. Every Christian believes that he has found salvation through Christ, but not all have explained that salvation in the same way.

Discovery is essentially personal. The thing discovered comes as a revelation to *you*: you will express it in terms which *you* can understand. Though we may, in the end, come to see the truth as we have found it in the historic Christian creeds, it by no means follows that the language in which they are couched is that best suited to this generation. For our own sakes and that of others we must seek truth that is fresh, unhampered by the past. The discovery will then be ours, and not even creeds will take it away. But there will be no experience of personal discovery if we *start* by seeking to mould our minds according to the dictates of some creed, church or sect. We must not treat Christianity as if it were a subject to be crammed for an examination.

Obviously there are pitfalls in our way. We may get at the kernel of the truth and yet, because of our prejudices, get it mixed up with rubbish—wood, hay and stubble—which we fondly imagine to be an integral part of the truth itself. This is especially likely to happen if we lack sincerity, or if instead of embarking on the adventure of finding truth for ourselves by the exercise of faith, we permit ourselves to think in authoritarian terms—asking whether so-and-so is right instead of asking what is true.

It is useless to expect complete agreement, then, amongst those who have new insights into religious truth. "There must also be factions among you, that they which are approved may be made manifest among you" (1 Cor. 11.19). The insights we gain are the test of our sincerity. In the scientific field we have noted (Chapter 10), that by careful thinking about faith it is often possible to distinguish between the chaff and the wheat. In religion the same applies. The man who refuses to think about or discuss his faith is often the man who fails to distinguish what is true amidst a host of false notions with which it has become encumbered.

The Simple Approach

But to obtain faith at all we must approach our problem with the innocent wonder of the child. Though we may have to think deeply at times and muster all the knowledge we possess, yet at other times we must allow ourselves to think as if we knew nothing. In this connection we remember how the great scientific discoverers had often to overlook the most assured knowledge of their day as a condition of making discoveries at all.

It may be necessary to read widely, as opportunity offers, but especially to read the Bible—the book which, more than any other down the ages, has brought a sense of certainty and conviction into the minds of men and women.

But it is easy to read and study in a way which makes discovery impossible. Any sense of following a set routine must be avoided. If an idea strikes us, we must be prepared to stop and think. "When I, at that time (1874), was going over the Wislicinus paper," writes Van't Hoff, "I interrupted my study half way through to take a walk, and it was under the influence of the fresh air on this walk that the idea of the asymmetric carbon atom came to me."[1]

[1] Quoted by P. Walden, *Journal of Chemical Education*, 1951, **28**, 304.

Wide Vision

One of the greatest difficulties in thinking is to see a problem as a whole. People who have been trained in science probably find this harder than do others. Students of the arts sense the atmosphere of the history book, or judge a novel by the general impression it creates. But in science we more frequently study the details. We have only to look through the titles in any recent issue of almost any scientific journal to see how extraordinarily specialized are the subjects treated. Men work for years on isolated pockets of knowledge, and it is not surprising if they sometimes tend to miss the wood for the trees. That, perhaps, is why it is so easy for a scientist to become carpingly critical when he turns his attention to other subjects. Here also he may tend to focus attention only upon the details and to reject important beliefs because he mistakes them for hypotheses. This is a point for which we must be prepared to make allowance if we have recieved a scientific training.

Direct Effort

The extraordinarily close resemblance that is found to exist between religious conversion and scientific discovery has not escaped the notice of professional psychologists. Thus Cole comments on the fact that great scientists, writing of their moments of discovery, use language astonishingly applicable to religious conversion, "whether the insight is given into matters divine or matters scientific does not seem to be psychologically important."[1]

Finally, we must remember that, as with all scientific ideas, direct effort will never yield an answer. We shall be mentally exhausted with the effort. But later the answer may come—suddenly and unexpectedly.

It will come, when it does come, apparently from without, as if it had been given us: we shall feel that we could never have sensed the truth by our own efforts. We have seen how this has commonly been the case in the great discoveries of science. And it is for the same reason that St Paul stresses as strongly as he can that faith does not come and cannot come through works—it is not the direct result of anything that a man *does*. It is the gift of God. It humbles us—the insight, when it comes, can never make us boastful.

The Bible promises that the new insight *will* come if we obey the conditions; there is no risk, as in science, that we shall strive endlessly without success. "If any man willeth to do His will, he shall know of the teaching whether it be of God or whether I speak from myself" (John 7.17). "Ask and it shall be given you; seek, and ye shall find; knock and it shall be opened unto you. For every one that asketh receiveth; and he that seeketh findeth; and to him that knocketh it shall be opened" (Luke 11.8).

Once again we note that it is implied that the answer comes from without—the door is opened to you from the other side, you do not open it yourself. On the

[1] L. Cole, *Psychology of Adolescence*, 1944, 2nd ed., p. 377.

other hand, it does not open if you do not knock. Again, Peter learns that Jesus is the Messiah, but not by his own efforts or clever reasoning. "Flesh and blood hath not revealed it unto thee, but my Father which is in heaven" (Matt. 16.11). But once again Peter, like the common people of the time, had been struggling with the problem.

Light, Certainty and Joy

When the revelation comes it is difficult *not* to use the metaphor of light in describing it. Scientists have used this metaphor freely, and the Bible does so too. People who lived in darkness saw a great light (Matt. 4.16); God's desire is that men may "turn from darkness to light" (Acts 26.18); St Paul speaks of "the light of the Gospel of the glory of Christ" and of the "Light of the knowledge of the glory of God" (2 Cor, 4.4, 6), and so on. Often Christ Himself is spoken of as the light, since the Christian faith centres upon Him. Other analogies are also used, though sparingly. The truth is a "treasure", a "pearl", etc.

When, after searching, a man discovers the truth, it comes with a sense of certainty. We have seen how scientists have described this certainty. Their language differs little from that of the Bible. "He shall *know* of the teaching . . ."; "We *know* that we are of God" (1 John 5.19).

We have noted how those who have received scientific intuitions have been filled with joy. Again, the same note runs through the New Testament. Jesus constantly spoke of His joy in which disciples were partakers. The Epistles are full of the same thought. "Having received the word . . . with joy" (1 Thess. 1.6); "Ye rejoice greatly with joy unspeakable and full of glory" (1 Pet. 1.8), etc.

Retaining the Fleeting Idea

We must particularly beware lest, when a fleeting idea has just begun to enter consciousness, we drown it and it is lost. This is not the time at which it is wise to discuss it with other people—we have seen how great discoveries have been lost that way. Nor is it the time to compare the new insight with what had gone before, since, as we have noted, new insights have a way of looking foolish by conventional standards.

But having found faith, it is vitally important that we should hold it fast. In early Christian days, a man who became a Christian made a public declaration of his faith by baptism. In our day opinions may differ as to whether an open declaration of acceptance of Christianity should take precisely this form—but of the need for a public witness there is no manner of doubt. It would probably be helpful to commit the new insight to writing as a means of focusing attention upon it—lest it retreat into the unconscious again. It would be reasonable, too, to join with others who share the same faith. The man who, having reached a state of faith, does nothing more about it—does not even tell his friends—will certainly find that the faith will die. The cares of this world and the deceitfulness of riches will choke the word and it will become unfruitful.

Very important, too, is the realization that, for the Christian, acceptance of Christianity is the beginning of a journey and not its end. Only too often the scientist who has made one great discovery, has not only failed to make another, but has failed to appreciate or rediscover for himself discoveries made by others. In like manner Christians who have made the discovery that marks the beginning of the road may forthwith become so stilted in their thinking that no new insight ever again comes their way. Like some of the early Christian converts, they wish only to be fed with the "milk" of the word, instead of the "meat" that is necessary for growth (Heb. 5.12). But the life to which both science and the New Testament call men is one of ever-unfolding truth, in which the exercise of faith becomes more rather than less important with the passing of the years.

Conclusion

We have come to the end of our journey. We started by asking whether faith is possible in a technological age when men claim that it is pre-scientific. We have found that Christian faith and even conversion are not alien to science—very much the reverse. The Bible asks no more of us than that we should use our minds in the same way as we should use them in science or in any other pursuit which calls for discovery and inspiration. "The word is nigh thee, in thy mouth and in thy heart"—these words turn out to be as up to date as when they were written. Scientists and saints use their minds in the same way.

To allege that science is a barrier to religion is to misunderstand both science and religion. It is to misunderstand science because it pictures the development of science as the mere adding of scraps of information to what is already known, rather than as an exploration of the unknown. It misunderstands religion because it pretends that religion makes calls upon us to which we cannot respond—in contradiction to the teaching of the Bible. Rightly understood, science and religion are seen not to be at variance but in the closest partnership.

Once foolish misunderstandings are cleared out of the way, we may be sure that the more we learn of scientific discovery and of scientific method, the easier we shall find it to discover for ourselves those truths of Christianity which make sense of our existence here on earth and supply a joy and a sense of purpose to life both here and hereafter.